Shape Up for Super Sex

Shape Up

MARY ANN CRENSHAW

with exercises by
Nicholas Kounovsky

Drawings by Gene Szafran

for Super Sex

DELACORTE PRESS/NEW YORK

ACKNOWLEDGMENT

Excerpt from WOMAN'S ORGASM copyright © 1975 by Georgia Kline-Graber and Benjamin Graber. Reprinted by permission of The Bobbs-Merrill Co., Inc.

Text copyright © 1977 by M.A.C. Productions, Ltd., and Nicholas Kounovsky

Illustrations copyright © 1977 by Gene Szafran

Designed by Giorgetta Bell McRee

Library of Congress Cataloging in Publication Data

Crenshaw, Mary Ann.
Shape up for super sex.

1. Sex. 2. Sexual intercourse. 3. Exercise.
4. Physical fitness. 5. Diet.
I. Kounovsky, Nicholas Alexis, 1913–   exercises.
II. Title.
HQ21.C69   301.41′8   76–41831

ISBN 0-440-07931-4

This is dedicated to the ones I've loved.
(Especially to you, Babes.)

Acknowledgments

It's pretty difficult to thank someone who has helped you do a book on Super Sex, now isn't it? The main reason is that most of the people who have helped me would prefer not to see their names here in print. Therefore, this go-around I'll be kind and leave names out of it, for my Rocks-of-Gibraltar know who they are and what they have contributed.

Other acknowledgments are so difficult, since there is no way to express the gratitude one feels for all of the people who help in the making of a book. I can only say that without them no book would ever come into being. A magnificent editor, an imaginative art director, a talented artist, a collaborator who knows his craft—each and every one helps to make the whole. The author puts it into words. To every single person who has contributed any single word to this book, I say, with everything in me, "Thank you." To Babes, I say I couldn't have done it without you. I never will.

Contents

Contents

SETTING YOUR PSYCHE TO SUPER SEX

The Name of the Game

Relax! This isn't going to be a sex manual. Mainly because manuals bore me and I never subscribe to any theory that has you making love with one hand while you have a book in the other. With this book, you're going to learn *how*. You're going to get rid of any anxieties you may have been harboring—perhaps unknowingly. You're going to be in physical condition to get into whatever position you find yourself in. You will not be told—ever—by me what position that *ought* to be, since Super Sex is a matter of what is super for you, even though it may not seem super to me at all.

So then what will I tell you? I'll tell you what condition you need to be in and how to get in it. I'll tell you exactly how to set your psyche to Super Sex and keep it set on that alone, for without the right mental condition, even our marvelous sex-oriented exercises could become mere calisthenics. That, neither Kounovsky nor myself will permit as he knows as well as I do that mind always matters. That's why I start Super Sex with exercises that set the mind at rest while they insidiously condition the body for Super Sex. Sneaky, but so what? I want you in shape for Super Sex, and I will make sure you are. Your psyche, your shape and your looks will all tell the world that *you know*!

First, I should let you know that you aren't being led into anything by anyone except professionals ... and careful how you read that!

Nicholas Kounovsky is the Russian-born, beautiful-body builder for most of the Beautiful People you have ever seen looking beautiful in the "in crowd." While I—well, I consider myself a rather accurate reporter with ten years on *The New York Times* in my background (the beauty and health scene was part of my beat) and I put together the now famous lecithin, kelp, cider vinegar and vitamin B-6 diet for my first book, *The Natural Way to Super Beauty*.

In *this* book—or rather, *for* this book—I've used my reporter's nose to scout out some fascinating facts about Super Sex and how to get it. A lot of what I've come up with are things that I thought everybody knew, but apparently only a few are onto. (Nosy reporters are among the privileged.)

One of the most fascinating things I learned is that so many hangups still exist in this enlightened era when it comes to the ever-lovely subject of sex. And yet, in a recent survey, *Redbook* magazine dug out the information that the people with the happiest sex lives have the happiest marriages. In short, the survey just reinforced my own belief that without happy sex, nothing is happy, and with Super Sex everything's coming up bouquets of roses.

As for just what makes Super Sex different from ordinary sex—well, here's where I may sound old-fashioned, but I believe that there are a lot of readers who are going to back me up. I feel that Super Sex is what happens when two people who genuinely like one another get into bed together, in shape for any physical machinations or gyrations, and then concentrate their entire psyches on *enjoying themselves*! The outcome should be an outburst. You will note that I did not say that they should just be pleasing their partners. That is because when Super Sex happens, partners are always pleased.

What makes Super Sex different, also, from some of the so-called "with-it" sex is that Super Sex is a one-to-one proposition. I am of the theory that once it is fragmented into sex with more than one partner, Super Sex is virtually unobtainable. As far as I am concerned, "kinky" is passé. Those who have experienced Super Sex—and yes, I'm one of them—know that it requires no gimmicks, no false relaxants, no aphrodisiacs, no unnecessary sex aids, no mirrored ceilings or water beds, no nothing except the putting aside of all you have thought about sex until you read this book, the putting in shape of your body so that you can physically do anything, and then the complete and utter concentration on pleasing your sexual self. Then, by golly, you've got it. And once you've got it, you'll never, ever give it up again.

There are some marvelous beneficial side effects to Super Sex that I might as well point out to you.

Super Sex shows in your figure. (Men, pay attention.) It's an absolutely proven fact that overeating is often a substitute for too little sex. Fortunately, the reverse is also true and too much sex not only keeps down the refrigerator raids, but also *uses calories*. How many, you'll find out in the Shape Section.

Super Sex shows up in your face. First, in the serenity that is going to come naturally after you've used the best possible relaxant—sex itself. Then, Super Sex will show in your skin, because the sexual flush is medically documented and real, and the blood that comes rushing to your skin and neck serves to cleanse and purify every pore, gives you the famous "blushing bride" skin. I've never seen man or woman whose face wasn't noticeably improved after good sex. I'm a reporter. I ask.

Super Sex even shows in your hair. Psychiatrists say that deadly looking hair is the first place depression shows and that's where they look. By the same token, I've seen deadly hair turn to lively hair when a lively life takes over. Don't ask me to document this medically because the medical men just can't. When it comes to hair, there's always a stumbling block. Just take my word for it—or your own mirror's.

Super Sex shows in your shape not only because it uses calories, and because you're no longer hungry for anything but sex, but it shows in your shape because the sexy exercises we're giving you are—while they put you in shape for sex—going to put you into terrific shape. They firm, they tighten, they stretch, they loosen, they relax and they were designed to make you sexy.

You can relax about the exercises. They aren't what you're used to finding in a book that contains physical exertions. They're developed to be easy, while they're putting you into the proper shape to take on the very best exercise of them all—Super Sex itself. All you have to do is have a look at most of these exercises to get the picture. You can see exactly what Kounovsky is aiming for in the exercises, and whether you do them alone or with someone else matters not. And who knows where —post-exercise—it may lead?

I threw in my knowledge of nutrition because you can't be sexy unless you're healthy. And, while I can't conceive of anyone's needing to diet on a lifetime diet of Super Sex, I've also tossed in, like a salad, the diets I consider to be the very best, healthiest ones, ranging from long-term to fast weight-loss—without, of course, any loss of sexual appetite.

When you have set your psyche to Super Sex, shaped up your body for Super Sex and looked in the mirror and seen Super Sexy looking back, then you'll know what you've got here in your hands. So I want you to read this book from front to back, then put it down, pick your partner and go to it. I believe you'll find it Super!

A REPORTER'S PROBLEM

I have been warned (practically threatened) that if I wrote a book such as this I would subject my family and my friends to humiliation —along with myself, naturally—and that I would undoubtedly lose my good reputation and possibly even my job. (Fortunately, my employers never came up with such a threat!)

I fretted and agonized a bit and worried a lot and arrived at one truth. The best possible reputation to have is that of integrity. There-fore, I decided to say the things I feel must be said in the only way I know how, with the hope that everyone will know I am doing it because *I* believe. And, if I myself enter into this book as a character, then it will be because it is impossible for me to write about anything in which I am not totally involved.

Therefore, assuming that honesty is the only policy, I place my life, sexual and otherwise, in your two hands, between the covers of this book. If anyone wants to throw stones, then let him . . . or her. But first, he or she must never, never move into a glass house!

CAREFUL

Right here I want to issue a word of caution—care and all that. We're giving you some wonderful exercises—some you can do in bed. Do them without fail. But *don't* do what I did, which was too incredible to be believed. It happened anyhow, so I may as well tell you so that it doesn't happen to you too.

Your author was seated on her bed. No, I wasn't indulging in sexual gymnastics, though I take The Fifth on what had preceded this incident. I was simply chatting with my partner who was sitting on the other side of the bed. Sitting cross-legged with my back to air. See what I mean? Care! Because the first thing I knew, somebody shifted (I always blame the other fellow) and I found myself pitching off backwards, head first! Talk about your life flashing before your eyes! It does. Instinctively, I tucked my head in and my legs flew over into the best back roll you ever saw, except that the crack of the neck could be heard across the room.

I was furious with my friend for not catching me. He thought I was simply showing off my gymnastic prowess. Now I ask you, who does a back roll from two feet off the floor onto one's neck? Only an idiot.

That gymnastic prowess, however, probably saved my life for, eighty dollars' worth of X-rays later, my neck was pronounced unbroken and the doctor pronounced that if I hadn't rolled, it undoubtedly would have been. Thank you, Nicholas Kounovsky, for all those years of training my instincts.

The very next day I phoned my interior designer to request some bed rails—hospital style. I think I need them.

The only point in telling you this story of my occasional non-equilibrium is so that the same thing cannot possibly happen to you. (Everyone wanted to know—doctors included—just "how did it possibly happen?" If I knew, it wouldn't have.)

When you are doing any exercises that require lying on the bed, for goodness' sake (or for your neck's sake) make sure that you are lying securely in the dead center of the bed—and lying—not perched precariously on the edge of your back to the open air.

OK. I've gotten across the point of my own stupidity. I just want to make sure it never happens to you. And if you ever drop from anywhere—well, by then, you'll be able to back-roll beautifully.

As for sexual gymnastics—try the floor!

The Sexual Sea of Tranquillity

As I sit here writing, I have before me the caricature of some poor, sagging slob—a caricature that illustrates a *New York Post* editorial on "The Age of Tension." In case you hadn't noticed, that's what we're all in together—the age of tension and hypertension, the disease that kills off countless numbers of Americans every day, heart attack after heart attack. Hypertension, according to the *New York Post* report, can be found, in varying degrees, in 15 to 33 percent of the adult population of the United States, or some 23 million to 44 million men and women. And, the report goes on to say that while hypertension is a broad avenue leading to heart attacks and strokes that has been heavily traveled in the past only by the elderly, it is turning up increasingly in the young, and even showing up in adolescents. When it comes to that, the age of tension had best be wound down.

Hypertension does not mean, as I once believed, "highly tense." It means that the tension has led the body to a state of elevated blood pressure to the extent that heart attacks and strokes are not only possible but probable.

I emphasize the definition difference because many must be as unwise as I on this subject. I recall being asked by an intern before a minor operation whether or not I suffered from hypertension. Knowing my high-key nerves, I answered "yes." Naturally he was surprised to find the super-low blood pressure I knew full well I had always had. Just a case of not speaking the medical language.

If your hypertension is real hypertension, you should be under your doctor's constant surveillance. If you are highly tense, you should still be under your doctor's constant surveillance, for any signs of oncoming hypertension.

There's another thing to be tried. You just might try looking at your mate in a highly sexual light. It could be the light that won't fail.

Dr. Eugene Scheimann, a physician who practices in Chicago, has written a book called *How Sex Can Save Your Heart and Life*. Bravo, Doctor! For Dr. Scheimann, it seems, subscribes to the same theory I do —namely, that nothing on this earth is going to reduce tension faster than sex. That it should be good and satisfying Super Sex should go without saying.

Dr. Scheimann comes right out and says it for me—namely, that love and sex (and you will notice that he equates the two—more on that later) *reduce stress.* He believes in sex as the great tranquilizer it is and he believes that pleasure—as in Super-Sexual pleasure—is a "boon to health, not a detriment." As Dr. Scheimann puts it, "Heart attacks strike those with too little pleasure in their lives, not too much."

Man, you can bet that's a doctor's prescription I can live with!

And not only is Dr. Scheimann with me on sex and tranquillity, but guess who else? WHO is. That's right, the World Health Organization, on January 10, 1976, issued their pronouncement from Geneva that sexual health care be designed for "the enhancement of life and personal relationships" and not just for dealing with procreation. In short, WHO endorses sex as fun and good for you as well. (When you get back to basics, what's fun is generally good for you anyway.)

Tense
or Ex-Tense

Ex-tense is how we want you, un-tense and ready to move into sexual action whenever the mood strikes. Your body is blessed with two marvelous sets of muscles—the extensors, which stretch and extend, and the flexors, which flex and tighten.

To make these muscles work as beautifully as any well-run machine, one set of muscles (no matter which) must tense while the other loosens. (I can only thank God that writing is my problem while musculature is Nick's!)

When I say "ex-tense," I mean just that. We want to un-tense you, for too-tightened muscles are the plague of your super-pressure society. Working to your advantage is the loosening up of your body, and in order to do that you are going to have to tighten up one muscle while relaxing another. However, Nick's exercises will show you exactly how to do it. Meanwhile, I want you to think of the agility of a cat. Watch it stretch. Stretching is just one way of loosening up too-tightened muscles that can cause tension and, ultimately, knotted muscles with plenty of discomfort to boot. In the next few pages we are going to show you exercises (no flinching, please!) both mental and physical, to stretch, limber and ex-tense every muscle in your body.

The exercises aren't going to hurt, they aren't going to be difficult, so don't cop out that way. They are going to make you into a pussycat—

male or female—and pussycats, as you may have noticed, generally have pretty active sex lives. And heaven knows, they're never out of shape for sex, if you'll take a look at the cat population-explosion.

We've devised ways—underwater exercises, for example—to make all that limbering even easier. You'll find that out when you arrive at that chapter.

One of the reasons I've been a Kounovsky pupil for half of my adult life is his understanding of the meaning of exercise.

Brute strength isn't always pretty. Check out some of the masters at weight lifting if you want to see what brute strength can do. Some of them can't even put their hands at their sides, since their muscles are so overdeveloped as to be practically useless for anything except lifting weights. (Give me a bionic arm any day that *that* sort of strength is required!)

In my classes with Kounovsky, the emphasis is on beauty, but—as I've often said before—softness, suppleness, effortlessness. We are never permitted to pant (yes, we breathe, and I am also going to tell you how you should do that as well), to perform jerky motions, to be noisy. I shall never forget witnessing the performance of one of the most famous ballet companies in the world recently. The prima ballerina sounded like Ann Miller (remember her?) at her tap-dancing best. I remember thinking that in my own gym class, the admonition from Kounovsky was always, "Don't let me hear you when you land."

Another point to know is when tension is required. Nick and I are going to show you that. There are going to be plenty of occasions when taut muscles make the difference between Super Sex or just plain sex.

This, however, is deliberate tension and should be worked on exactly as we show you. And we will show you exactly. Don't try to show off and do more than we ask. That's simply defeating the purpose. In my opinion, Kounovsky is the ultimate authority on when to loosen, when to tighten, when to tense, when to be relaxed but always ready. If it's hard, it's wrong, and he and I will make sure it isn't hard—meaning, I hasten to add, difficult.

RELAX!

We're on the way to that nirvanic state. There are a couple of Kounovsky-isms that are the key to the success of your relaxation, and

I suggest that you imprint them on your brain before you begin:

No violence! That is the thing I am bombarded with class after class. Those jerky, too-fast movements are probably a hangover from a harried day at the office. I, for one, move around my office as if I were on skates (good idea, too) and find it exceedingly difficult to turn on to "soft" when class time comes. It is the thing I am working on hardest at this time. I think even Nick himself is surprised, although he still berates me for answering the telephone too swiftly. (Writers' phones ring often and loud.)

In other words, any rapid, jerky, fast movements are detrimental to the exercise itself—and, needless to say, to all it can accomplish. Fluidity, softness and *slowness* are the keys to every single exercise in this book. It isn't how fast you can do them, it's how slowly and softly you can that determines whether you get a pat on the back from Nick or not.

One more thing. Breathing is supremely important, and this book will tell you how to do that properly. I should have said "two more things," for I have never been in a Kounovsky class where we were not admonished with the words "a pleasant expression would be helpful."

It's incredible to watch the student in full exercise-progress chuckle at these words, and then to see all muscles relax with that chuckle. The expression on your face matters indeed, for a relaxed smile indicates the softness and relaxation we are after. A clenched and determined jaw simply, as Nick points out, puts into work muscles we don't need to use, causing more work than necessary. Check it out as you go. If you are grimacing with pain, then let up on the exercises so that they are less of a strain on any muscle. If you are grimacing even though nothing hurts—and chances are that's what's happening—then you are back to creating stress. The answer is to let yourself go—mentally and muscularly—right into our hands.

You'll emerge a different person in both body and mind.

It Feels S...o...o Good— How to Work Out the Tension

We've already shown you that tension wrecks your love life. Not the tension of muscles, but the tensions of life. Remember that article on "The Age of Tension"? Guess what the conclusion of the study was? The best possible way to relieve tension is by some sort of physical activity. Certainly Kounovsky knows that and always has. I envy him his life, which revolves around physical activity. It is his passion, but then there are those of us—like myself— who have worked at overpressured places, such as *The New York Times,* where we were faced by a deadline a day.

Pressured people are the ones who find it difficult to let go at day's end. That is why I make certain I make it to my Kounovsky class at the ungodly hour of 7:30 P.M. whether I get there on hands and knees or not. At least I get there. And when I leave, invariably it is with a springier walk, a smile (one of the Kounovsky requirements), and a generally more relaxed and more energetic feeling.

As Nicholas Kounovsky so aptly puts it, however, "The dosage of relaxation should not create a vacuum"—meaning that we don't want you to fall asleep when there are other, more fascinating activities that are by now—I hope—on your mind.

Nick says, "While loosening the joints and limbering the body, relaxation should set up every muscle for vitality and stamina." My translation is that you should be ready to go on to Super Sex (and how!) once you have rid yourself of any negative tensions.

The study in the *New York Post* recommends jogging or sanding furniture as two of the best remedies for getting your mind (and body) turned off of stress. But something tells me that what you will learn in this book is a hell of a lot more fun, and never forget it for one moment. It has the magnificent plus of putting your shape into super shape while you're at it. So now you're on to relaxing the exercise way. How much more could you possibly want?

Wear as little as possible, and make sure you're comfortable (whether it's on your bed, on a soft rug, or wherever you choose). Then loosen up everything, starting with your wrists and ankles. Do each of the

following exercises slowly and rhythmically. Begin by doing each exercise at least twice, working up to perhaps six.

For wrists and ankles: Lie on your back with your arms and legs in the air (the young lady in the drawing is doing it perfectly). If you aren't that flexible then bend your knees a bit. Slowly flex and extend your hands and feet.

You see? We begin at the beginning, which is at the extremities. You'd be surprised how every muscle begins to let go when those wrists and ankles are unknotted.

Breathe consciously but *always*, when exercising, inhale through your nose and exhale through your mouth.

You'll be surprised how often you find yourself holding your breath, so work on breathing with a steady, slow, relaxed rhythm as well.

For elbows and knees: Lie flat on your back with your arms stretched above your head, legs straight. Slowly bend your left elbow and your right knee at the same time, trying to make them meet. Don't be upset if they don't. Then do it the opposite way. (Never, at any time, do we want your beautiful body to be one-sided!) Then extend back to where you began.

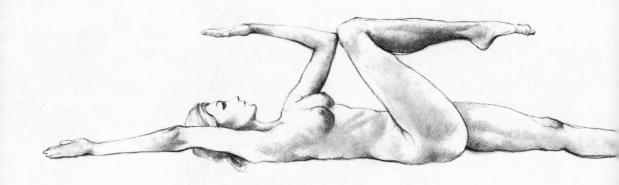

For shoulders and hips: Still lying down, put your arms and legs in the air (again remembering that you are allowed to bend your legs if it hurts—we all have different areas of flexibility). Slowly move your left arm and leg forward and your right arm and leg back. Keep alternating. Make sure you breathe out—through your mouth when legs and arms are up—and inhale when they are open.

Feel it in your hips and in your shoulders? Any idea how you plan to use those muscles? If not, think about it and read on.

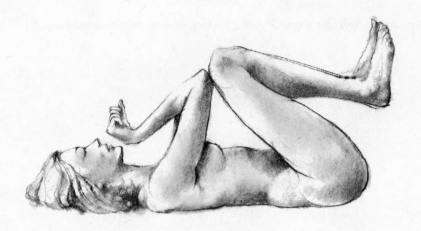

For every joint in your body: Still on your back (hmmmm!) bend
your arms and legs in a crouching position. Don't forget to exhale. Inhale while you very slowly extend your arms and legs and spread them.

By this time, your joints should be "together." (You see, there are
other kinds of "joints" to relax by!)

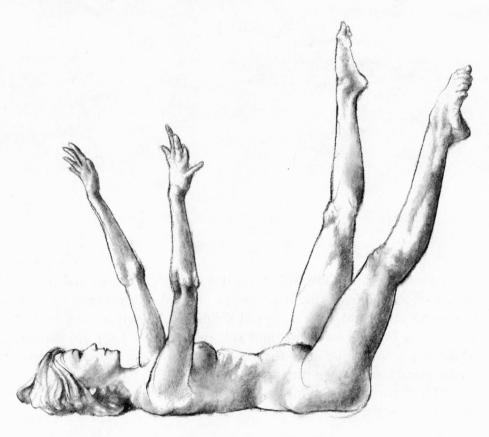

This one's for the flexors—things that tighten up when you want things to be tight, or loosen when flexibility is what counts. In Super Sex, it may jolly well be flexibility that counts, depending on which way you like your Super Sex. If it's agility that's required, this exercise will see to that!

In a semi-sitting position, lean back on your hands with arms slightly bent. Lift one leg and try to reach your foot with the opposite hand. Remember, always inhale when you extend your body, exhale when you compress it. (It's an easy thing to remember, since the lungs, smart organs that they are, tend to press out the air when your chest is compressed.)

For the body extensors, which make you as lithe as a pussycat (men, don't feel left out, for male cats do OK), do this: lie on your stomach with arms bent as if you intended a push-up. Slowly extend your arms, arching your back ever so gently. Bend your right knee and try to touch your foot with your left hand. Don't expect to do it this well—at least not at first. But you can see from the illustration exactly what is extending. While you're doing that, you're working on the muscles of the buttocks (which you will surely need), the pectorals (no explanation needed here), the back of the leg and the front of the upper leg—all of which should be dead giveaways as to their importance in the super-

lativeness of your sexual performance. Once you've tried it with one hand and foot, do it the other way around for symmetry.

And always, but *always*, remember this: when you arch (or are extended) inhale deeply through the nose; when you lean forward, Wheww!—let it out through the mouth.

By this time, if you've gone at it as slowly and surely as we say, you should feel the kinks coming out. The new "kinks" are the ones you may want to put there on your own, in bed. That's your thing! For us, the problem is getting the muscular ones out.

The Rules of the Game

What rules? Isn't it nice to know that sex is one game where you invent the rules as you go? It's great for me, since gamesmanship never was my strong point, and I hate following rules, don't you?

There is only one thing (call it a "rule" if you must) to remember if you plan to join the rest of us in the game of Super Sex. That "rule" is: enjoy yourself!

You will note that I said "yourself" and it was intentional all right. If you are enjoying yourself to the hilt (hmmm!), and your pleasure is showing up as a super experience, then there is only a very slim chance that your partner isn't experiencing the same pleasures. Don't stop to look—or ask—please! You'll break the Super-Sexual spell. Later, over a post-coital cigarette, you may ask him or her if it was fun, but while you are into Super Sex, be only into Super Sex.

My feeling is that the very only way to satisfy your partner is by satisfying yourself completely. That's the reason for "yourself" with no guilt attached, and it's one time when you're not only allowed to be selfish, but you've got someone—me—practically ordering it.

It is only by enjoying yourself that your sex is going to be super—meaning active, active and more active, but never passive submission. When you've learned (which I hope you will) to stop worrying about who's had an orgasm—and when—and gone to carrying on with whatever is simply terrific for you, that's when you're en route to a lifetime of Super Sex. Pleasure is contagious, as you'll quickly discover.

When you begin your Super Sex life (now!) you ought to know what you can expect. What you can expect is intensity. I can remember practically having to be peeled off the ceiling on many an occasion (I have a superman, as usual, around the house), and on most occasions I don't remember anything at all. That is because every fiber of me is so involved in the very act of giving pleasure to myself (and thereby to my man) that all other senses are simply gone.

Don't worry. I'm not a medical oddity. All sex researchers will tell you that intense sex (i.e., Super Sex) creates an absolute black-out of the senses of hearing, smell, awareness of anything except sensations in that part of you that's involved in the Super Sex. Which is, of course, just as it should be.

It's also another reason that I do not believe in orgies. Any diversion from so intense a preoccupation as Super Sex would render Super Sex impossible. You might get sex, but you can have that anytime. There is simply no way to concentrate that much energy, nor force that much concentration, onto more than one target at a time, so orgy-goers can argue the point with me till the cows come home, but I still say they've never known Super Sex—as you will! At least not at orgies.

Those Fucking Positions!

Guess what? You've found a sex book that isn't going to tell you what position to take on anything! Anything, that is, except Super Sex, which I will not only tell you but practically order you to be enthusiastic about.

As for sexual positions—well, I, by golly, am going to let you work those out for yourself. The exercises will put you in shape for whatever shapes up as the position of the moment, and from there on, you're on your own together with your partner. Leave me out. That's where I should be. Out of your minds, momentarily. And on your mind should be nothing but Super Sex and your Super-Sexy partner.

I suppose you've guessed that this chapter has hit another Mary Ann Crenshaw rabid-act. If there's anything in this world guaranteed to turn me into a monster, it's a sex book that presumes to tell me which way to turn when I'm making love. You see, I think that's strictly up to me and my man.

Damned if I'll keep a book by the bed and ask my partner to wait while I turn a page to see where his arm and my leg ought to be at that particular moment in time-to-orgasm. Screw it! (Actually, there are better things to screw than books, so "phooey" is enough said.)

Back in 1926, when the most famous marriage manual of them all, *Ideal Marriage* by Th. H. Van de Velde, M.D., was first published, it was a breakthrough from the sexual secrecy that surrounded the age of Victoria—in spite of the fact that the Victorians were the most libertine of the lot.

Ideal Marriage was first a liberation, and later a hangup. It could have been called, irreverently, the book of liberations, since all of the permissible positions, or what Dr. Van de Velde considered to be acceptable sexual positions, were given in Roman numerals—such as position IV, i.e., "The Attitude of Equitation (Astride)." It may take awhile for you, as it did for me, to figure out that this is simply the good, old dame-on-top method.

It's all terribly pristine, but it sure isn't clear, since I've studied and studied and don't understand a whit. I've probably tried positions up to XXXX and just don't know the language.

Now, in the nineteen seventies, this business of numbered positions, some of them downright acrobatic (please remember my own acrobatics and remain careful), has become somewhat ridiculous.

As I've said, I don't want any bloody book interfering with my own Super Sex. And interfere is what they seem to do, these manuals with numerous and well-numbered positions.

In most cases they do a lot more harm than good. Physicians tell me that the most famous manuals often do the most harm. One doctor swears he's seen more marriages ruined by belief in manuals than by any other cause . . . and he goes on to cite the case of a young couple who were patients of his and on the verge of splitting up their own marriage. It seems they just couldn't make it on position LIV or something. Fortunately this was one intelligent doctor (he should have become a shrink) and he said to them, "For God's sake, are you crazy? . . . You've got one of the best sex lives I've ever heard about!" I later heard that they didn't split up, meaning they gave up reading marriage manuals and decided to go on their own instincts as to whether or not their sex was super.

I am sure that Dr. Van de Velde not only had good intentions but that his intentions had good results in his day. However, a colleague of mine—the one who put me onto *Ideal Marriage* in the first place—wrote me the following note after I had questioned whether *he* was the one who claimed the book was responsible for his divorce.

The note says: "Where in hell did you get the base canard that I had a copy of Vandevelde [*sic*] while I was married? By the time I got married, I had read Vandevelde and was no longer interested in instruction manuals, only in practical demonstrations."

Bully for him. His marriage might not have made it, but his interest in sex did, and he didn't do it by the book. I'm for that.

As an apology to Dr. Van de Velde, however, I will tell you the following anecdote. I will swear that this one is true and it involved one of my mother's best friends.

Seems that a crowd of country-club bridge ladies somehow became involved in a discussion of sex. (Somehow, everyone seems to become involved in a discussion of sex.) This friend, in her peculiar, wonderfully drawling voice, said, "You mean, there's more than one way to do the damned fool thing?!"

So you see, there are those who need advice on positions, although I can only pray that they put the books away before bed. There is one kicker to positioning, however, and that is that there may be exactly *one* position that is positively perfect for both you and your partner. If that's the case, I say, why research any more? In short, what suits you two suits me.

We're Coming—
Get Ready—
Put Your Pelvis in Shape

Face it. Any one of you who has already enjoyed Super Sex knows that—no matter how well conditioned you think you are—you're going to come away from that bed-session a wee bit sore. I think it's terrific because it simply reinforces my theory that sex is, after all, the very best medicine—as well as the easiest to take.

On the other hand, you want to be in condition to take it. These exercises will see to that.

Obviously, the pelvic region is the one that's going to get a pretty good workout all right, and so are the abdominal muscles (I like to call them the "abominable abdominals") and so it's a wise person who's sure he's/she's in shape for Super Sex by getting those muscles in super shape first.

Nobody wants you giving out in the first round. Therefore, here are some goodies for strengthening the abdominal girdle (so that no one needs to wear one) and the pelvic region which, I might add, includes the inner thighs. Once again, the use of the inner thighs for superior sex should be pretty obvious to all. If it isn't, never mind. You'll have them in the shape they should be in after these:

Sitting back on your elbows—as if you were lounging on a beach—bend one knee slightly. Keeping that knee bent, slowly (that's the tight-

ening part) raise and lower the other leg, keeping that leg as straight as you can. If you can't get it as high as shown here, please don't feel left out. Not too many people can—at first. Do this several times and then

do the same thing with the other leg. When that straight leg goes up, exhale (remembering you're compressing your lungs) and inhale when you lower it.

For a skinny waistline, lithe and flexible, try this: Sit up halfway, leaning on your right arm, your left arm at eye level—both arms straight. Bend one knee and inhale. Raise the straight leg, trying to touch your hand. If you don't make it at first, then don't raise the leg quite so high . . . just high enough to feel it. After all, it's results you're after, so don't cheat yourself by making it all *too* easy. As you raise your leg, exhale. With this one, you twist the waist and should feel it. Pretty soon you should feel your clothes getting looser around the waistband as well. Just one nice side effect from getting in shape for Super Sex.

Sitting down, try to balance holding your ankles. Then slowly, slowly extend your legs upward, maintaining your balance. Exhale. Still holding your ankles (and doing your best to keep your legs straight to attain a "V" position), separate your legs to stretch them sideways and inhale. Repeat this one several times and slowly come back to the balance you started with. This one's going to work on making your hips able to balance in any position (**I** hope you get the implication) and besides that, will do a lot of stretching for the inner thighs.

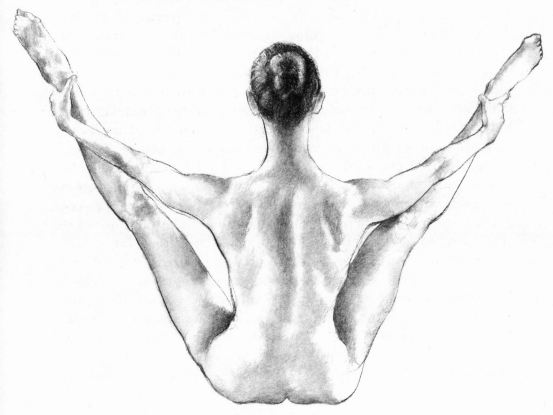

Pussycat, Pussycat

No obscene thoughts, please. The pussycat I have in mind is the infinitely female, inevitably blonde and beautiful, cuddlesome creature one always sees snuggling up to innumerable men . . . in pictures anyway. Especially in advertisements, where they're more often than not going on about how they make sure they get enough iron, or don't let their husbands (and they're always "husbands") have less than bright-and-white shirts.

Still, they're pussycats, no doubt about it. Just what I always wanted to be except that fate cut me out to be more a tart-tempered tabby with a strong streak of self-sufficiency. That self-sufficiency all by itself is supposed to be a turn-off for men of any virility whatsoever. The only thing is that it doesn't really work like that. Luckily for me. In my less-than-humble opinion, it takes one hell of a man to make a pussycat out of a tigress, and one hell of a man is what every Super Sex-seeker needs. There's strength and there's strength, and I remember well one of the old-time advertisements that always emphasized "strong but gentle." That gentleness is what I emphasize, more and more and more. Women respond to it, and I've never heard one call a man "weak" because he was tender. It's the old "machismo" number that's practically guaranteed to be a turn-off to any thinking woman—and most are, these days.

As far as I, personally, am concerned, a man who makes a crude grab for me the moment he enters my door is more than likely never going to enter (that door or me) at all. In fact, a husband/wife team of doctors have written a most unusual book called *Wake Up in Bed, Together*. They are Dr. Claude Nolte and Dr. Dorothy Nolte. Dr. Dorothy Nolte expresses her own feelings about the "abrupt" approach occasionally used by unthinking (and probably well-meaning) men. She says, "A woman can experience abrupt movements as a 'personal violation,' especially when that's the *only* approach she receives."

She says it for grabbing, as far as I am concerned. I don't know whether this is a reaction peculiar to women or not, although I have often been tempted to grab one of these "machismo" types by the crotch at some unexpected moment, just to see his reaction. I'll bet that reaction would not be erection, but more probably fear.

Therefore, dear gentle-men, do not be surprised if your woman does not react with pleasure when you grab (and I mean grab) her bosom while she's holding, for example, a skillet full of hot grease—just likely to spill onto *you*, don't forget! I have said there's no set time or place for Super Sex, and I don't renege on that. But there is most definitely a time *not* to touch, and most certainly not to grab. Try a little tenderness. And watch out for hot grease! It could ruin you for life.

On the other hand, if you want that pussycat woman that all of us women want to be—deep down inside—you'll find that there are plenty of ways to tame a tigress. Super Sex is the sure way.

Taming the Tigress

This tigress—and I like to think I'm at least 50 percent normal, though my friends may disagree—has maintained all of her life that, in spite of the "difficult" tag sometimes attached to me, she (meaning me) can be tamed by one easy rule: that of the three F's.

When I mention them my family will disown me, my friends will pale (if there are any left by now) and, who knows?, perhaps all my former employers will disown me too. Never mind. The three little words that can help tame most tigresses are:

Fucked

Fondled

Fed

The "fed" may seem a bit odd, so I'll save that for last.

The first, and most important, "F" should be obvious. Haven't I said all along that I truly believe that good sex can cure anything that ails one? I have some awfully powerful psychiatric backing on that theory too. It brings us back to the business of relaxation. Lord knows, I am not a relaxed person by nature, running mostly on nervous energy and remaining the bane of Kounovsky's in-class existence. Trying to concentrate on being soft, soft, soft while in a high state of nerves isn't easy. But after a good session in bed, I become the pussycat I always wanted to be, and the purring is practically audible. Simply because sexual intercourse always has been, always will be, the greatest tension-easer of all time, while it goes on being the best shaper-upper, the best health-giver, the best heart-protector, the best longevity-security—you name it, sex does it. Super Sex is always best, but even so-so sex is better than no sex, as long as it's a regular thing. And, to use an appropriate cliché, you're getting a treat with your treatment.

And there's your first "F" for taming tigresses (or tigers).

Fondling is something else. I must confess that there are some people who claim to hate it. I don't understand them at all—people who can't stand to be touched—and I can't help feeling there must be some psychological something behind such a reaction, but that problem belongs with an analyst, not with me.

For those of us who do like—and understand—touching, there's nothing more pleasurable than plain old fondling. Drs. Claude and Dorothy Nolte say, "If you think the wish to be held is 'childish,' consider that thought a hang-up you could do without." They explain that skin-to-skin contact that involves being held or stroked by one's mate is a powerful and legitimate human need. And they go on to say that many women aren't even searching for sex—just cuddling—which is a need they found even prostitutes confess to having.

Fondling—as in a delicious backrub—can generally reduce me to jelly and put me right in the hands that are rubbing my back. Usually it doesn't stop there.

The third "F," which is food, is my own special problem because I have that not-so-rare disease, hypoglycemia, or low blood sugar, which means that if I'm not fed on schedule I get irritable, mean, and turn into a wildcat, not a pussycat. (Before anyone says it's all in my head, let me hasten to assure you it's all a matter of medical record.) Since more people seem to be discovering that they have this disorder, I would imagine there are more hungry tigresses than one supposes.

I do not mean, however, that one should eat heartily just before a lovely love session. One of my old lovers always swore that Attila the Hun died that way. He (my friend, that is) had an obsession about waiting four hours after eating. I could have died waiting!

No, I don't want you to eat heartily . . . just enough to take the edge off the temper. Lean and hungry is the best way to be in bed. But mean and snarly is what you don't want, so I, for one, quickly nibble something to turn off the shakes (a hypoglycemic symptom) if I feel myself getting snappish. Anyway, you're going to need all the strength you can get for Super Sex, and you certainly don't want to take a nasty temper to bed with you. Therefore, if the grumps inexplicably descend on you, think about the third "F" and check out your blood sugar with your doctor. If it's low, you'll know.

The simple fact is that humans need to be loved, need to be caressed, need to be cared for. The three F's satisfy every need. The man who remembers them satisfies me.

Making Waves—
Exercises to Do
in the Tub

In a recent *Late Show* TV re-run of my favorite James Bond flick, *Thunderball*, there was included a marvelous and typical Bondian scene. As you probably know, *Thunderball* was practically an underwater, scuba-diving flick. In one magnificent scene, 007 and his chick disappear behind a coral reef, there is an enormous flow of air bubbles, then a switch to the relaxed couple reappearing on the beach, with Bond saying, "I hope we didn't frighten the fish." Don't ask me how they made it through all that rubber gear, but, of course, to Agent 007 nothing is impossible—especially if it's sexual.

Well, now I understand that the latest kick in sexual activity is underwater intercourse. For years I heard it was impossible until I tried it to see and—well, it was pretty damned terrific. They say the weightlessness gives it a new dimension. The only other way to achieve weightlessness is on the moon, and I don't know of any shenanigans there, though who knows what happens in the zero-gravity trainers where the new lady astronauts are being indoctrinated.

So be it. Suffice it to say that water has always had a certain sensuousness about it. Just being near the surf, wearing as little as possible, usually brings out the horny in everyone.

Showering together is standard—and sexy. I do not advocate doing anything more strenuous than lathering one another unless you wish to drown. But the warm bath . . . that's something else. Underwater games are something else, and underwater sex is something not to be missed. For those who call it impossible . . . wow! What they're missing! Just ask me.

UNDERWATER WORKOUTS

Can you think of any more sensual way to relax than by soaking in a tepid tub? Maybe you like it hot. I do. Some like it cold. Nick tells me that a friend of his fills a tub with cold water and then, when he gets in, "it boils." Wish I knew that friend!

Nicholas, however, informs me that mildly warm water is the best temperature for relaxing everything, and I must confess that I do find hot stimulating (that's why I use it) and ditto for cold. So, when it's relaxation, not stimulation I'm after, I will, from this day forward, stick with warm.

Fortunately, a tub of warm water is also the best possible place in which to do those marvelously relaxing exercises that make everything loose enough to do anything without snapping. I think you know what I mean!

In any case, there's something to be said about the tub, *first*. Just make sure that you haven't got soap all over the place. It could just cause you to slip and really break something—and that we do not want. It always helps to have those rubber strips on the bottom of the tub, even if you're a quick-shower addict (which I am, unless it's relaxation and stimulation I'm into the tub to acquire). Nick says, use a rubber mat. I say it's imperative. We don't want accidents.

Rub-a-dub-dub, two in a tub, slippery with soap or simply being close, warm and wet is about the most sex-appealing way a couple can be. Little wonder, then, that we are going to show you things to do in the tub, if you aren't otherwise occupied, to make it all even more fun.

One thing is super-important. Take time to enjoy all of this. Savor the warmth, let the tensions go down the drain, do these relaxers easily and slowly and remember that everything—yes, everything—is easier underwater. It does, as you doubtless know, make your own body weight a lot less, meaning there's less of you to lift.

Stretch! Sitting in the tub with one knee bent, raise your arms and one leg (toes pointed, please). Now flex, flex, flex your wrist by making a fist and then spreading your fingers while you bend your ankle first one way, then the other. Feel the tension leaving? It has to.

Don't forget to keep breathing (after all, your head's above water) and then switch to the other leg and foot.

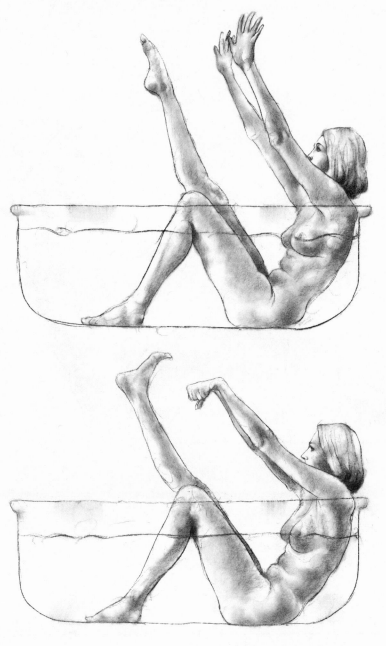

This one's for the inner thighs and is meant to tighten them up. You will need that for sure. You want a good grip on anything within your grasp. So: Sitting in the tub (holding onto the edges for stability), hold a washcloth between your knees. Slowly squeeze several times (thinking each time about something other than a washcloth). Hold for a few seconds each squeeze. It's the holding pattern that tones the muscle. You'll see.

For your pectorals: (There are more uses for a washcloth than its maker ever dreamed of.) Still sitting in the tub, making sure the water's warm, put your feet on the rim of the tub and hold the cloth in your hands. Slowly squeeze (a sponge here may be better), contracting your pectoral muscles. Move your arms from side to side, squeezing all the while . . . and breathing, for goodness' sakes . . . or rather, for your pectorals' sake.

This one is bound to get you in the upper thigh—luckily, since the upper thigh is one of the most important spots to have muscles strong enough for a Super-Sexual life. Ditto for hips, and this one does the same thing for both—it makes them firm, strong and ready for action!

Kneel in the tub and sit back on your ankles. Put your left hand flat on the bottom of the tub and hold the edge of the tub with your other

hand. Contracting your hips and thighs, slowly raise them out of the water. At first you may need a bit of help from your arms. Later try to make sure it's your hip and thigh muscles doing the work. You'll feel it enough to know the difference. And remember that when you feel it, there's where help was needed.

Inhale as you come up, exhale when you kneel down. Now repeat, changing arms.

This time the backs of the thighs get it. And well they should. Remember, your thighs are going to be supporting an awful lot of weight during an awful lot of your Super-Sex life, and, unless you wish to just lie there and have a mediocre sex life, it's best to have every muscle toned up and ready.

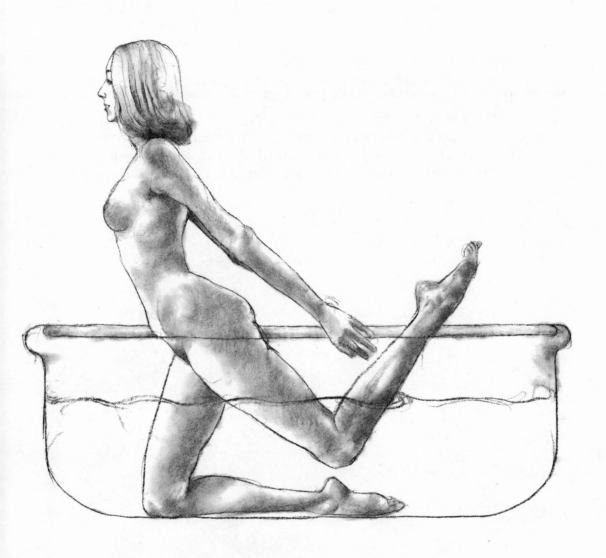

Kneeling in the tub, sit back on your ankles and grasp the rim of the tub with both arms.

Slowly rise out of the water (Venus on the half-shell, or something), lifting your left leg back and up, keeping your knee bent all the while. Straighten your arms to get a bit of help from them and exhale!

Still working on those legs, here's the best way to get in and out of the water: Holding the rim of the tub, bend one knee, keep the other leg straight and slowly lower yourself into the water, bending your elbows, of course. Exhale going down.

Then try to get back up by the reverse process, using the same bent leg.

Don't forget to proceed to the other leg.

In fact, *always* remember, even if it's hard the first time, never, *never* leave an exercise until you've worked on both sides of you equally. Unless you plan on some pretty one-sided sex. Different, but not super.

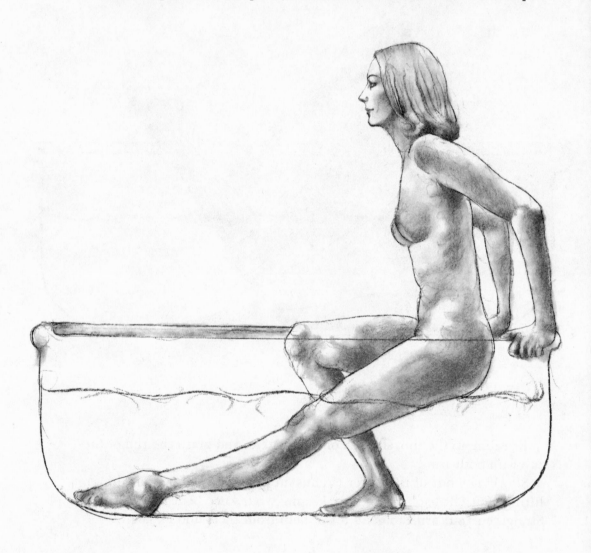

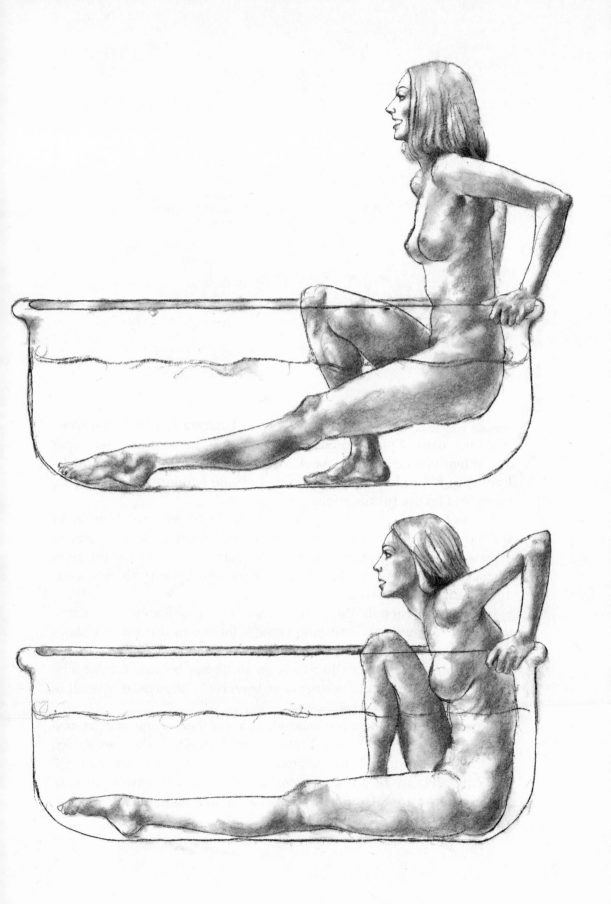

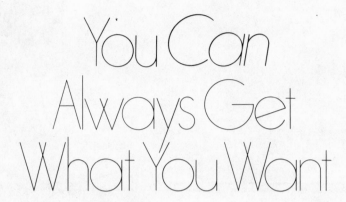

You Can Always Get What You Want

hen I started this book, everyone asked me, naturally, how I could presume to be an authority on Super Sex. When anyone starts *any* book, that kind of question always is asked. I am sure if I did my own memoirs someone would ask how I could presume. I ignore the question.

Except for you out there. I'll let you in on the secret. I was born lucky and have remained so all my life. I've never had a lousy lover, Latin or otherwise. There's probably no such thing as a bad lover for the right partner, and I'm one of those romanticists who believes there's someone out there for everyone.

In any case, though I've run across a few less-than-perfect lovers, they've never stayed around long enough for me to learn much about their hangups—mostly because they weren't invited.

Therefore, I presume to do a book on Super Sex because I owe everything to the Super Sexual partners I've been lucky enough to have all of my life.

Now all you have to do is look at me to know that *anyone* can get *anyone* he/she wants. God knows, I wasn't born beautiful. (I've seen uglier, but I have a feeling it doesn't matter at all.) I was called "Dick Tracy" as a child because of my beak nose, and I confess it wasn't pleasant. As an adult, I found out what did and didn't matter, and you can clearly see I haven't succumbed to the pleadings of all the plastic surgeons who see the ideal nose job when they see me.

The way I figure it is that nature, as always, is a whole lot smarter than humans. You, as a sexual person, will doubtless project the vibes, the electricity, the scent (or whatever goes into the vague and evasive mystique known as "sex appeal") that will bring an appealing person into your life.

I remember a time when a friend, who always bet me I couldn't get this man or the other—and dared me to try—did it again. I had set my cap for a co-worker who was, shall we say discreetly, involved. When I mentioned my intentions to my daring friend, his reaction was "Impossible. Preposterous. You'll never be able to seduce *that* one!" Ho! Not until his involvement left town for the summer. Guess who was on the phone inviting me for dinner that first Saturday night? Don't think for a moment I believed it was dinner he was asking for, and so, of course, I wasn't a bit surprised when he brought me home and said, "I'm staying." He stayed for the whole summer, too . . . one of the nicest of my life.

As to my disbelieving friend—well, I'm beginning to wonder now whether or not he saw himself as more than a friend. I never did and so never gave it a moment's thought. Perhaps he wanted to be next. I'll never know.

The point is you *can* always get whatever you want if you decide to have it and make your desires (and availability) known. It shows on your face.

The man I've been with longest is a classic example of how you can get what (or who) you want by setting your cap and keeping it on. We met by colliding in the street one hot summer New York night. He was with my best friend. I was sandwiched between two giant men. No matter. The "zap" that was felt by us both eliminated all the competition and from that day on we've never been apart. I take that back. We've been apart but we always come together. Over sex.

I must confess that once or twice in my own life I went against my own relatively straitlaced (don't laugh!) grain and seduced some man just because that certain friend, whose habit it was, bet me that man was unseduceable. No man is *that*. Neither is any woman. Or at least I hope not, unless they wish to miss the most beautiful part of life itself—sex.

The point is that if *I* can do it, anyone can. There is only one thing you have to remember. Sexy is as sexy thinks, which means that you'd best be thinking about sex most of the time.

All of us go through periods when we are overworked, tired, down, and just plain aren't interested. Those are normal periods of human sexual hibernation, and they disappear in their own time.

But if you think about sex, and the way you want it to be, that is the way it is going to be and no one can stop you once you've zeroed in on your target. Just make up your mind to have it and have it you will. I promise.

A dear friend of mine is involved in a fiery romance with a Latin lover that is a far cry from her seven-year pseudo-marriage with an older man. (The seven-year itch seems to be a reality in some cases, and apparently all was not well in their non-marriage bed.) In short, she was bored.

And so she looked and found and came up with what sounds to me like a winner. (I've never believed that Latins are lousy lovers, having spent much of my sexual life with foreigners—no idea why.) This young woman—who's always been that beautiful blonde I would like to be and am not—now says that she's never attracted so many men in her life as she is attracting right now. Right now when she's so perfectly satisfied at home. I can only say what I believe to be the cause: *because* she's so sexually satisfied, her once-hidden sexuality is showing to all the men on the make. I used to wonder why a looker like this one couldn't get *anything* she set her sights on, but I guess the mind has control over us all. It's only when you *feel* sexy that sex is going to flood your life. And it's going to be super.

Maybe the feminists didn't know what they were doing when they started the bra-burning bit, but if taking off your bra makes you feel sexier, then by all means do. Just be sure your breasts can stand up to it (mine can't, but I wear the flimsiest thing possible). Do anything and everything that makes you feel sexier. But the most important thing of all is to think about sex a lot. And consider masturbation. That will help keep it on your mind.

I've just finished interviewing an extremely well-paid call girl (the price she gets made me think of changing my profession, but I fear my selectivity would get in the way), thinking that I should consult the pros for some tips on things I might not know.

She devoted a lot of time to spelling out all the kinds of things one must do to oneself to attract a man. Guess what? Boy, do I have some tips for her! Now, what on earth is the matter with me? I wouldn't pretend to stack up to this one in looks, and probably not in experience, though perhaps my experiences were better and therefore more valuable.

In any case, my friend, the call lady, spent an awful lot of time on the kind of perfume one needs, the necessary pre-coital bath, and, specifically, the kind of clothes one must wear in order to appeal to a man.

Well, my dear lady, I haven't forgotten a few years back when I managed to seduce one of the most screamed-after heroes of the moment —a boy about thirty years my junior. I lusted after this beautiful young creature, all right, and I must say, he whispered to me on the dance floor, "How nice to find a *real* woman." Don't know what his previous experiences had been, but they must have been *in*experience.

In any case, you won't believe it, but I'm shy. Besides that, as the movie-light of the moment, he was chaperoned and chaperoned and chaperoned. I hadn't really planned on seduction until a friend assured me it couldn't be done. Once again, that did it.

My ploy was pretty direct. I told his chaperone I was taking him home for a nap, and then I told him the same. His chaperone's reaction was, "Fine." While his was, "You are? Terrific."

That's not the story, however. This little seduction scene was quite unplanned, but, as it was our hero's last night in town, it was then or never for me. As luck would have it, I was wearing my most tattered pair of underpants. Like most people in the fashion world (and I was), fashion is often the last thing on our minds. Besides, they were beat-up enough to be the most comfortable ones I owned. When we got down to seduction he asked me, "Why are your knickers [you can tell he was English] so ugly?" Might have thrown some ladies for a loop but I simply explained that they were comfortable that way. So what? The seduction scene was magnificent. Must prove something about having, or not having, the right underwear.

In fact, my current man said to me, in the beginning of our relationship, "You have the tattiest underwear of anyone I know." I promptly rushed out to buy seductive and beautiful things. A few months later, they too were tatty. The man and I are still together.

Perhaps the funniest thing that ever happened to me, in the middle of a big love scene, was during the midi-skirt era—remember that?—when laced boots were de rigueur fashion, and, as a so-called "fashion person," I needed to show that I knew, at least, what fashion was.

Quite unexpectedly, my dinner partner of the evening, who, I thought, hadn't the least interest in me, apparently had lust as well.

He escorted me to my apartment and, after making it clear he intended to stay (in this case, I was delighted), proceeded to remove my clothes. Horrors! I had completely forgotten that beneath those lace-up boots—which took forever to unlace—were hidden a thick pair of knee socks—the better to avoid boot-blisters! I think the only thing that saved me that time was the fact that I'd forgotten my underwear. Skirt comes off to reveal lots of me, boots, and knee socks. Whatever it was, the result was obviously a turn-on for him. The problem was in getting him to go home. Ever.

These little vignettes should say a lot about whether or not a man is going to go for your body *because* of your underwear or in spite of it. We all want to look our best, of course, but then sometimes seduction is unexpected and all of your best lingerie just might be in the laundry. *Never* consider that cause for turning down any desirable proposition. If you're the woman you are, he won't be looking at your underwear.

But then perhaps that's why I'm not a call girl but merely a woman who likes men. (And I emphasize the word "likes.") You see I don't believe that clothes make the woman. It's the other way around.

Get Ready for Whatever Comes Along— Exercises for Flexibility

I once had a performing leg—one that always went out of whack when I least needed it to. Well, Kounovsky says it all has to do with limberness, which helps you avoid muscle spasms (like mine) or cramping. I mean, it's really not very sexy when you think about it—to leap screaming in pain from what ought to be a bed of fun. Therefore, try these exercises on your bed for future bedtimes.

For flexibility both forward and backward: Kneeling on your right knee with your left leg straight out in front, bend your body forward as far as you can and exhale. Then shift your weight forward onto your knee and arch your back, head back too, arms too. Inhale, of course. Then change to the other knee. When you can do this perfectly you'll be as supple as a snake. I don't know about the sex lives of snakes, but I do know about the advantages of suppleness in bed. So get on with this one fast!

To stretch those ever-important hips: At one end of the bed, lunge high and place one foot on the bed in front of you, keeping yourself securely balanced with your hands. Gently bend your knee, lean forward and exhale. Come back to a standing position and repeat with the other leg.

This fixes trick legs like mine (thank you, Kounovsky!), making you limber. Using a corner of the bed, sit in a split position with the right leg forward, the left leg back—*both straight*. Gradually move toward the center of the bed for more and more stretching—*carefully*. Keep breathing normally. Then change to the other side.

This one's called "the scorpion," and while I don't know about the sex lives of scorpions (I do try to stick to human males), it would appear they know something!

Lying face down on the bed, toward the end, hug it (the bed) with your arms and raise your legs upward and wide apart, as high as you possibly can.

Then try to bend your knees without lowering them.

After this one, relax for a moment and let every muscle loosen up.

As always, inhale when you lift up, exhale while you're relaxing. Repeat this a few times and a scorpion will be envious!

Balancing on your upper back, put your hands on your hips to support you, leaning on your elbows. Then split your legs with right leg forward, left leg back. Now bend both knees, slowly. Now change legs.

Sex Is the Best Exercise— After These

What these exercises do should be obvious. You can jolly well see what necessary muscles you're going to develop to get what you want and make the most of it. And, I can almost assure you, even though you practice and practice, you are still going to be sore after sex *if* you do it right. I've been a student-gymnast for twenty years now and no matter how much muscle I aim for, there's simply something about sex for toning up muscles that can't be beat.

I had a rather amazing conversation with a friend the other day. She's into a new love affair, and, of course, that means sex every second they get together. Over lunch I asked if she were ever sore the day following. The answer was negative. I'm getting to be a regular snoop, following everyone's sex life and taking notes . . . even on my own love life. Since this young (and she is) lady is not the athletic sort, one has to wonder whether or not she's the passive sort—which is not the right sort for Super Sex.

You may be sore after you first begin to tone up, but even if you become Olympic material, I hope you'll be sore after sex. If not, then I'll bet you're not working as hard as you should—at Super Sex, that is.

Sit on the floor with your knees bent and feet slightly apart, arms behind you straight with fingers facing in toward your body. Exhale.

Slowly raise your hips to form a bridge. This one should get you in the thighs where you want to be gotten. Try to lift your right leg with knee bent, and inhale. You should feel this one in your buttocks, your arms, your upper thighs and you should feel strong, strong, stronger for it . . . the better to assume some new positions in life. Now do the other leg.

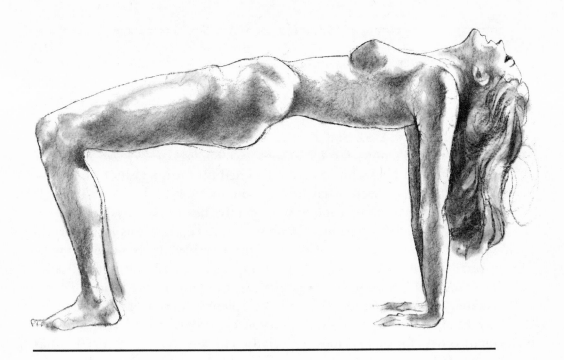

Did you ever think you'd do a headstand? Neither did I until I met Nicholas Kounovsky. As a child, I was most emphatically un-athletic. Could be because I had no one I could trust to teach me, and without that, one could get hurt. Not being big on pain, I simply didn't try until I hit New York and Kounovsky's studio my first week in town. Having read his now-classic textbook, *Six Factors of Physical Fitness*, I signed on with Nick almost before I signed up for my fashion courses—which supposedly were what brought me to New York.

And guess who taught me to stand on my head? Kounovsky. But you know what *really* taught me? Alcohol. That's right. It was in my drinking days (I don't touch the stuff now) and I arrived at class one day with a terrible hangover. I was simply too tired to fight off a headstand, thinking, "Oh, hell, so I fall. Might ease the pain in my head." To my amazement, my attitude made me completely relaxed, and I stood on my head, solo, with no effort whatsoever. I have found that, as with many other things, and most especially with sex, fear of failure is what *causes* failure, while total relaxation—which is why I keep telling you to relax and breathe—makes you perform feats you never believed possible.

However, since you *aren't* at Kounovsky's, you must do this exercise in the safest possible way, which is in a corner against a wall. That way there's absolutely no chance of your falling unless the wall falls. If it does, sue the building. We have shown this exercise as done by an expert—so you can see all the angles. Don't you try to get off the ground —yet.

Crouch in a kneeling position with your palms up, one hand over the other to form a sort of cradle. Put your head inside that cradle, using your hands for support. Your elbows should be bent on each side of your knees, toes curled in. The closer you can get your knees to your head, the better it will be. Harder but better.

With arms, head and hands staying put, straighten your legs—as straight as you can get them.

Raise your right leg as high as you can. Then bend your right knee.

This isn't a headstand yet but a preparation for one (don't say you were unprepared), so get used to it. Your legs are going to feel it—I hope. Your pectorals most certainly will, so think of the lovely bosom, and the back of the legs will soon be able to stretch long and straight without pain. Great. Painless sex in any position, I always say. No pain, period, I always say.

When
What You Want
Isn't Around

Many years ago a doctor friend of mine called to say that he *had* to tell this story or he would explode. Keeping the name fictitious, in orthodox medical manner, he explained that a patient of his had just been in to see him with the question: "Doctor, will masturbation hurt my arthritis?" The doctor was a bit taken aback since the patient in question was around seventy-five years of age—which means nothing, I hasten to add, when it comes to sexual activity. However, the doctor, knowing the man was happily married, replied as sedately as he could, "Why no, Sam, it won't hurt your arthritis, but what about your wife?" To which the man (and I certainly won't call him "old man") said, "Well . . . we make love four or five times a day but sometimes that just isn't enough." At which point, my doctor friend's mouth doubtlessly fell open.

Not only had the gentleman blown the doctor's mind with his sexual proclivity, but he'd also hit on a taboo as well.

That taboo, it seems, is masturbation, though I'd like to venture a guess that rare is the soul who doesn't do it. It would seem, however, that no one is willing to admit that fact. Masters and Johnson, in the course of their sexual research, found that something like 90 percent of those questioned admitted to lying about masturbation.

I will come right out in favor of it.

Face it. Masturbation will never replace a partner. Nothing will. On the other hand, there are times and circumstances that make having a partner an impossibility. (Perhaps the gentleman whose story I have just told is a case in point. Doubtless his wife was exhausted!)

Sometimes it's a clear-cut question of one partner's sex drive far outracing the other's, and nobody said that one is good and the other bad. In fact, finding partners with exactly the same sex drives would be akin to finding your identical twin somewhere out there. It just isn't too likely to happen. When it does (as sometimes it does) count yourself lucky indeed.

I will never forget watching a panel show on television on the subject of the many sexual problems of desperate people . . . or perhaps I should say it was about people desperate to have their sexual problems (real or imagined) solved by the panel of experts. Experts they were, too, including leaders of sex clinics, psychiatrists, psychologists, etc. This was a show that accepted telephone calls from listeners. At one point, a pathetic call came in from a woman who recently had been widowed. Her question was, "What shall I do for a sexual outlet, as I am young and my sex drive still functions?" I wish you all could have seen the panel parlay their devious routes around the question of masturbation.

Every single one of them told her it was perfectly OK to go out and find another mate. Not one of them admitted—nor did it seem to occur to them—that the lady was grieving and so did not *want* another mate. At least not just then. The experts went round and round the question, with the mediator trying, futilely, to lead them to the obvious answer. These experts weren't about to be led. I, personally, was tempted to call in with a few choice suggestions of my own.

And one of my suggestions would have been what the poor lady was hoping for—namely, the go-ahead signal for masturbation.

The simple fact is that masturbation is not going to hurt you. As one insistently anonymous gynecologist puts it, "It feels good." It *is* a substitute for a partner when you haven't got one, or when, at any given moment, you don't want one.

It will not give you acne, cause you to go blind, or grow hair on the palms of your hands.

As far as I am concerned, any person who says he or she has never masturbated is probably lying. Whoever hasn't experimented with masturbation is missing one way to learn a lot about one's own sexuality. And if you don't know about your own sexuality, then how do you expect your partner to know. That's an important point about Super Sex. Your partner *won't* know unless you tell him/her or unless you wait for some who-knows-how-long period until the right combination comes up. The chances of lucking up on that combination's appearing without your help are slim indeed.

Therefore, anything that helps one know oneself helps one's sexuality. When it comes to masturbation, it's every person to his/her taste. Manual masturbation is one obvious solution. Most women find that any pressure against the clitoris can bring on an orgasm. Marital bliss would appear to have no effect whatsoever on the use of masturbation as a pleasurable sexual outlet. Sometimes the partner—however satisfying—simply isn't available when the need strikes. And no partner should assume that occasional masturbation by his/her partner implies he/she isn't doing everything right.

Whatever your method, I simply want you to relax in the knowledge that the world is with you on the masturbation matter. It's a legitimate outlet for pent-up sexual longings, and a lovely relaxant as well. Find yourself your own private place where you can do with yourself what you will. And then find out how sexy you can be when you try.

I have only one word of warning and it occurred to me when I heard an absolutely hysterical story at, of all places, my haircutter's. (Come to think of it, that's the place you hear *most* stories!) Fortunately, I've known everyone at the salon forever and they're always onto what mischief I'm into—therefore I get the anecdotes, thank goodness!

This one went so: It seems one of the guys who works there once worked for Blue Cross. He swears that he processed a form wherein the claimant maintained he had lost a great part of his penis to a vacuum cleaner! I cracked up, but I can't imagine it was very funny to the victim. Apparently he had to have plastic surgery and a skin graft, which I would imagine would make his future sex life less than super.

Later in the day, I related this saga to a friend of mine who said calmly, "Oh, yes, that's the ———— Suck." I refuse to name the brand—no lawsuits, please.

All I can say is it's some brand, since my own vacuum cleaner barely picks up dust.

Apparently everyone was onto the vacuum cleaner trick but me, so

I must be dense on certain subjects like mechanical masturbatory marvels.

The January 1976 *Penthouse* published the following letter from a urologist which I will quote verbatim:

"As a urologist I see the end result of many indiscretions. Young men, it seems, often have an unfathomable urge to couple with something—anything. The outcome is seldom as tragic, however, as befell a young man who had heard of the supposed thrills a vacuum cleaner could provide. I was called to the emergency room to see him shortly after he had mounted an upright, inserting his penis into the side port for suction tools. 'Suddenly there was a flash, awful pain, and blood everywhere,' he recalled.

"The result was sickening to behold. Despite a two-hour operation to repair the damage, he must undergo two more operations to restore the urethra. Because a large blood vessel was severed, the end of his penis will never get hard again. Certainly for now his penis is neither useful nor ornamental.

"Several of my colleagues have cared for such injuries recently. Apparently the risks don't get publicized.

"Anyone contemplating the use of a vacuum cleaner fetish [*sic*] might consider retaining a urologist in advance. Name and address withheld."

I wish they hadn't withheld the name and address in case anyone out there is stupid enough to try such a trick. But tricky is what tricky gets, so for the sake of your sex life, don't mess around with vacuum cleaners.

MORE ABOUT MASTURBATION

When I mentioned the matter of masturbation, I had no idea what I was getting into. Seems there's been a screen of silence around the subject for years. How am *I* to know? I have very open friends—or at least they are when they talk to me—and I know what I myself do. So, you can imagine my surprise when, suddenly, I was confronted by a friend of mine—beautiful, young, married, mother—who told me that she has never masturbated. I reeled. And, of course, asked her why the hell not!

She said because she didn't know it existed! This whole conversation came about because I was laughing over some chapters I had found in one of my many manuals in which the title was "Beginning Masturbation." And, as my man jokingly said, going on to "Intermediate, Expert and possibly even Remedial Masturbation."

I had found the whole idea of "courses" in masturbation so absurd as to be ludicrous. And yet here was this perfect girl telling me she never knew.

Therefore, I must retract my statement that I believe anyone who says he or she doesn't masturbate (probably more "shes" than "hes" here) is lying. I believe this woman. But what has she missed?

The No-Ring Circus

Performance. How often have you heard that word associated with sex? It's a word I'd like to see barred from everyone's sexual vocabulary, for it implies that one or the other of you is on view, with a perfect "performance" expected.

In the pleasures of sex, there is no such thing as giving a performance, and, therefore, very little way the supposed "performer" can give a bad one. All rave reviews, we hope.

Still, it seems to me that all too often we find the old ratings system still at work when it comes to "sexual performance." And such a system is pretty much guaranteed to turn off all the fun.

If there's one thing I hate it's the woman who delights in regaling her friends with the sizes and shapes of all the penises she's known. It doesn't take much of this sort of woman to make one want to escape her kind.

I have in mind one particular woman—now happily (she says; he says nothing) married—who managed to back me into corners all too often to complain that virtually none of the men she knew could "get it up." I would imagine not. For there's another phrase that implies a performance—and a judgment that if the man doesn't "get it up" on cue, he should roll over and die. We women are lucky because if on any given night (or day) we *really* aren't up to it, at least it doesn't show, and we do have the option of pleasing our partner anyway. That in itself is pleasurable if one gives a damn about the partner.

Years after I finally rid myself of the rantings of this particular woman, I found myself going out with an ex-lover of hers. He allowed as how she was quite right. He certainly couldn't "get it up" . . . with her. Fortunately he was able to "get it up" just fine with any other woman he knew.

Therefore, before you begin to use such pronouncements, consider this: could it be you? I am quite sure this woman never considered the matter at all. But I will confess to being curious as hell about her marital sex life. Oh, to be a fly on the wall—just once.

Forget about the performing arts unless you happen to be in the theater. Sex is a game for two (in my opinion) and not open to criticism.

Getting It Up, Down, Sideways— Exercises for Body Control

You want to be ready for anything, don't you? Upside down, right side up, wherever your inclinations lead you? Then *gradually* (and please note and respond to that word), work on exercises like this one. It will improve your circulation and your (as Nick puts it, in his charming Russian-English) "body control." That is what you most certainly want for your new, Super-Sexual life.

Now try to do the other side.

I am going to take a moment to say once more just how important it is to breathe correctly. I found myself holding my breath while doing a handstand in class one day. Miraculously I stayed up there, but I would have done a lot better had I loosened up enough to breathe naturally. On the other hand, a gentleman in my class went through a difficult exercise without taking a single breath and, P.S., he failed. I have a feeling he'd have done it—given a little air. Therefore, breathe consciously. It's that important. If you can hear it, you know that oxygen is getting in, and also out.

This works on practically everything. It's relaxing. It's stretching. It's putting thighs and groins where they belong, meaning stretched out to the fullest. Go gently at first, for this exercise is as good as you make it. Once again, don't feel put down if you can't make it perfectly in the beginning. I assure you that practically no one does—not at first, but soon. The results will be well worth the effort.

From a kneeling position, sit down on your ankles, head in your hands and relax. Point your toes (always prettier) but keep everything else loose, loose, loose. It's the old curl-up-in-the-womb routine. Breathe deeply.

Slowly, curl your toes under, raise your hips and straighten your arms.

While you hump your back, straighten your legs as much as you can. Our illustration shows it done perfectly.

Now move your head inward and look at your knees, keeping your legs as straight as you can all the while.

Bend your left knee to the chin and then straighten your leg upward, elongating the body as much as possible.

Inhale going up, exhale coming down.

Now do the same with the other leg.

And bravo!

The Severed Head— Impotence Conquered

If only one could separate sense from senses, then the curse of male impotence might be removed forever—to virtually everyone's relief.

I myself have been frustrated by the potency of impotence especially when it turned up in the most sexual man I know. I will say, thank God, that I met impotence and dealt with it effectively, but it is the most delicate of all love-making situations, and a man, finding himself suddenly and inexplicably unable to make love, no matter how much he wants it, is the most pathetic and vulnerable of all human beings. To see the panic rising in the face of a man who realizes his penis isn't going *anywhere* is a torturous sight indeed to any woman who loves him, and can see that panic is the only thing rising.

If there is a woman out there who would put down a man who, on such an occasion, cannot "get it up," she will most certainly get what she deserves: no sex and probably no man. For one thing, I hate the very connotation of his having to "get it up." Something tells me that if the woman is doing *her* part with proper care and enthusiasm, it is going to be up.

And, if for some extraordinary reason, it isn't, then chalk it up to the fact that the head—meaning nerves, anxiety, tension, and stress—is generally the only thing getting in the way. There is, of course, such a thing as clinical (meaning medically caused) impotence, but it is rare indeed. Most of the time it's all in a man's too-active head.

A man in such a position needs all the love, care and sympathy he can get, and any woman who berates him for the condition is severing the wrong head. She should cut off her own!

First, a woman has to care enough for her man to give him all of the love and encouragement he's going to need at such a moment—and that moment comes to 90 percent of all men, sometime in a lovetime.

How does a woman deal with impotence? My own (and I might add, successful) method has been that old trick of attack and retreat. The more attention called to the condition, the more of a condition you've got. Never, but *never*, mention the subject of impotence, no matter how frustrated you may feel. For once, don't consider your own sexual feelings, because it's the long-run you're after. You'll benefit more from the cure. Talk about the weather, the movies, probably not the stock market these days, but about anything except sex.

Then, when he's least expecting it, zap him! I once actually pulled a light karate chop to the throat of my lover when he tried to restrain me from "doing with him what I would"—to get erection and, finally, ejaculation. Fortunately for me, he didn't remember that chop to the throat, but it startled him enough to make him forget his panic and go on to a normal finale.

Happily, I have no hangups about oral sex, and you'd be surprised how many men who are, temporarily, impotent will respond to the touch of a tongue. I find it difficult to understand the person who could consider his/her partner's genitalia "dirty." To a person like this, I can only say, if you care enough about someone to be in bed with him at all, then there's not a single spot on his body that you should consider dirty—unless, of course, that body is dirty for real, in which case you've obviously either chosen the wrong partner or should convince that partner to bathe more often.

Later, we'll have an entire chapter on the delights of the tastes and odors of the human body, but for the moment, rid yourself of the idea that any part of anything you love isn't wonderful, pleasurable and well worth embracing. Because embracing is one of the most important cures for impotence that you will be able to take an "I did it!" pat on the back for.

If taking a man in your mouth—just for now—is going to restore him to his former virile self, then, for heaven's sake, go to it. You'd probably be surprised to know how many men long for this and haven't the nerve to ask. It doesn't speak too well for the understanding quality of females, does it? But then men are perhaps the weaker sex after all, in some areas. It behooves you to take the initiative.

I believe in fondling. Fondling implies caring, and medical science has long proven the importance of fondling to infants. Well, I've obviously never come out of my infancy, because, to me, fondling is one of the most important things in life and certainly one of the things that proves a man cares for me, particularly when he doesn't necessarily expect sex as his due reward.

Don't ever think that men haven't the same infantile (so what?) desire to be cuddled. And fondled. If you run up against a man who claims he hates to be touched, I'd be willing to bet he doesn't object to having his penis touched. And if impotence is your foe, then make sure the man in question knows you're fondling for the sake of fondling and because you like the feel of his penis, hard or not hard. Once again, any woman who gets in bed with a man whose body she doesn't like— and that means every hairy and/or unhairy part of it—had best re-think her motives. The body beautiful means the body that appeals to you.

Note I said, "fondle," not "grab." I have never forgotten the lesson I learned with my sometimes-impotent man when I touched on his penis and had him tell me later that he was impotent because he felt I was grabbing him to see whether or not he had an erection. (Now you can see why, occasionally, I would like to sever *his* head. Temporarily, anyway.) That just didn't happen to be the case. I touched it because I loved it, but he reacted as if I were testing him and so, of course, the love-making that day was zero. Moral: make sure you touch fondly and gently, for apparently men have the same feeling about "grabbing" that Dr. Dorothy Nolte pointed out women have. Make sure he knows you enjoy touching him because you like what you are feeling and that no reaction is required. As someone said, wisely, "A man can't be up all the time." Neither can a woman, but it's easier for us to hide it . . . or so they say. I have my doubts, supposing that imaginative lovers know whether or not their partners are turned on. What they *must* know is that it doesn't matter. Love is never the same from one time to the next, and *that* is the most important lesson to be learned about sex.

A relative of mine (and this was at the turn of the century, so relatives, don't panic!)—the most virile man ever—had his own bout with impotence, I am told, when he was in his late teens. Fortunately, he had a very wise doctor. The doctor sent him off to work on the railroads—not blue-collar work, but hard-hammering rail work. You see, physical exercise (and that's why relaxation exercises work on unexpected things) is the one guaranteed antidote for nerves. The part of the brain that works during physical exertions—and this means heavy exertion —is entirely different from that used in mental activities. That's why one is often more tired from a day's work at the office than from a swift game of tennis. And certainly more tired than from a particularly exerting roll in the hay.

My "impotent" relative's doctor knew his business all right, for, I am told, this young man realized he was cured when a beautiful blonde crossed his path one day and—well, you can guess the rest.

I have also counseled (who am I to counsel?—except that I've apparently had plenty of experience with the impotence bugaboo and come out the winner every time) other friends with the same problem.

Women's liberation had done its bit for the impotence which appeared without warning in a very dear friend of mine. (Counsel, here I come.) He was a recent divorcé, with one of the primary reasons (so both parties say—don't ask me to confirm) that his wife simply couldn't keep up with his super-normal sex drive.

Divorce was the unfortunate consequence, although I am sure there is more to the story of an unhappy marriage than sex.

In any case, my friend found himself free to make all the love he wanted—he thought. However, he had married young and spent a lifetime relatively sheltered from the new, liberated ways of the women's world. On his first post-divorce date, the girl said, "I want you. Will it be your place or mine?" Sounds like a line from a movie, but he swears it's for real.

Naturally, this man was thrilled. Gee!—sex just like that, and without even asking. Need I tell you that when they got into bed, and I don't know whether it was at his place or hers—he couldn't. Little wonder. Her come-on would be enough to turn anyone off, just as she would probably react adversely to that old "grab." It took a lot of talking on my part to convince this friend, of whom I am particularly fond and about whose virility I have no doubts whatever, that impotence is a sometime thing. The best thing he could do would be forget it, forget sex, and one fine day he'd have it—hopefully with someone a bit more tactful. P.S. He did. One more case cured by separating sense from senses. Which is the only sensible way.

Tighten Up!

r. Sheldon Cherry is a New York gynecologist of great repute, with a couple of books of his own under his belt. He was kind enough to present me with one, which, I might add, caused some consternation when I appeared with it at *The New York Times*. Its title is *Understanding Pregnancy and Childbirth*. Oh well, "Let them wonder" has always been my motto.

Dr. Cherry was kind enough to block out a half hour of his valuable time to help me out with the problem of inner musculature—a subject that's going to be super-important to every single female reader of this book. That problem is the one of keeping the vagina in its virginal, naturally tight condition.

I have never forgotten the (regrettably now retired) nurse of my own doctor who taught me about diaphragms. She also warned me, "Mary Ann, use the cream or jelly but be careful not to use too much. After all, you want *some* friction."

Right. If a penis slips in and out of a vagina so easily that the man doesn't know he's been there, and neither does his partner, then there simply isn't going to be much enjoyment for either one.

There are rare cases, I am told, in which a vagina is deformed, meaning that it is so large it must be corrected surgically. There are also rare cases where the vagina is too small, but that is, more often than not, a good case of vaginismus—the tightening up for no entry—that is the result of fear, anxiety, nervousness. All the things I intend to see you'll never have to worry about. In the unlikely event a vagina is too small, it is correctable by stretching or by surgery. That, however, isn't something I think many will need to consider.

The problem of a vagina that has been stretched in childbirth, and allowed to remain in this unhappy condition because a careless woman didn't do her post-delivery exercises, is a problem indeed. Whatever the reason, there is a way to correct it and a relatively simple way at that.

When I asked Dr. Cherry the question, "How do you keep your vagina in shape?" he answered by saying, "You should ask the pros." Don't know what got into me—closet innocence perhaps—but I didn't quite understand and when I asked him to explain he said you keep it in shape "by having sexual intercourse."

Dr. Cherry says that *active* sex is the best possible way to keep the muscles surrounding the vaginal area in condition. He maintains it's the same as with any other muscle—with the biceps, the triceps, the abdominals, the pectorals. Because any muscle that isn't used is going to atrophy and become useless, while any muscle that is used regularly (and I certainly emphasize the regularity of sex) and properly is going to be in fine fettle.

There's a side benefit to keeping this particular crowd of muscles (for they are a group) in shape and that is that the exercises that work for the vaginal muscles also work for the elasticity of the bladder. It sounds unattractive to talk about leaky bladders. However, as one grows older (and don't we all, if we're lucky?) the bladder tends to grow weak, or flaccid, meaning it isn't so easy to control the urine. I'm going to come out and say it now. You don't ever want to be wearing rubber-lined bikinis, so work on your bladder health while you work on your sexual proclivity. The exercise is the same, and when you're ninety, you'll thank me. If I'm still around.

According to Dr. Cherry, the vaginal muscles, technically known as the levator plate, are comprised of three to four muscles that surround the three orifices that "make up a woman's pelvic support." That's about the best medical description I have ever heard and I am giving it to you straight because Dr. Cherry very kindly sent me a clip from a medical journal on vaginal exercises and the causes for vaginal weaknesses. I didn't understand a word. I do understand, however, where a woman's bottom is and what the three orifices are: the urethra, from whence cometh the urine; the anus, and I assume you know where that is; and the vagina.

The levator plate more or less forms a sling around all of these openings. These are the muscles that one wants to keep tight, all for obvious reasons. To be blunt about it, the first two hold in urine and bowel movements.

The levator plate, however, contains the very muscles that tighten, or contract, the vagina. And when the vagina is contracted, which can be at will, sex is infinitely more pleasurable for both parties. According to my expert, Dr. Cherry, some women—after learning the exercises—have become adept enough to separate those muscles that tighten the sphincter muscles around the anus from those that control the bladder from, finally, those that control the vagina. And, furthermore, he maintains they can feel all three as independent entities.

Terrific. It may sound a bit like Tillie the Tassle Twirler but one thing I can guarantee firsthand. The more you can control the vaginal muscles, the more you can control sexual enjoyment for both yourself and your partner. As Dr. Cherry said, we all stand to learn a lot from those who make a living at making love. Obviously, they'd *better* be good.

In any case, the doctor confirmed what I keep saying—that a woman who is active sexually is much more stimulating to a man.

Nobody—including me—wants you simply lying there, for there's neither fun nor fitness in that sort of sex. You can lie down alone any time, and will, unless you put your heart and muscles into active sex.

The exercises that are going to keep your vaginal muscles—in fact, that whole group of levator muscles—as tight as the day you were born are easy indeed. I found to my surprise that I'd been doing them all of my life, which just might account for the fact that my doctors always pronounce me in perfect, elastic condition. I'd been doing them for pleasure, but so what? I'm more than happy to find out they've contributed to my healthy sexual state.

I will let Drs. Nolte and Nolte give their own medical description of how to do these exercises . . . exercises which are traditionally and universally prescribed for women right after childbirth. But they should be done forever and ever to preserve the part of you that is going to preserve your sexuality and make your mate reach for you instead of anything, or anybody, else.

Drs. Nolte explain that the quickest and easiest (Dr. Cherry concurs) way to improve the function of the vaginal muscles is to learn to control urination.

The Noltes suggest that you sit on the toilet to urinate and shortly after you start, stop the flow. Be sure there's no "dribble," for if there is, your control is far from controlled. The best control of all is when you can stop the flow of urine midstream—meaning that if you really are desperate to pee, and are able to stop halfway, then you've got it made for vaginal muscular control.

They say you should not have to squeeze your buttocks together (I haven't noticed that it matters) but we agree on one point: the exercise alone is sexually stimulating.

They go on to recommend—and again I concur—that you practice contracting your muscles during the day (believe me, no one will notice unless you have a beatifically happy expression on your face—in which case, nowadays, everyone will probably think you're potted). They suggest twenty-five times per day at least. When you hear that some women can reach orgasm by this sort of stimulation alone, you may be more intent on your homework. I don't care what makes you do this exercise. Just do it. It's going to make Super Sex for everyone.

An Orgasm Is
an Orgasm Is...

Well, what do you know? Someone has finally defined an orgasm. Pretty good description, too, so I'll pass it on to you verbatim. Before I do, however, let me tell you—just so there'll be no anxiety anywhere—that *no* orgasm is ever the same twice. It's like snowflakes. Nature, once again, has confused us humans (and we know better than to try to fool Mother Nature) by doing the seemingly impossible. Because orgasms, in a lifetime, are never going to be exactly the same way twice. I think it's nice myself. I get a surprise every time. Sometimes it's gentle, sometimes it's jarring, sometimes it's gut-racking, but it's always, always great!

One other thing to get unanxious about. An orgasm isn't a prerequisite to satisfactory sex. Many will doubtless doubt. Don't. You'd be surprised how fulfilling it is to a woman just to be filled by a man, and if, for whatever reason, that day an orgasm doesn't appear, it's no tragedy. It will, when it's good and ready. Just remember that Super Sex requires such things as fondling—remember?—and often fondling is more important than orgasm.

But back to our description of orgasms. This has come from a book called, imaginatively, *Woman's Orgasm*. I only find the title amusing as it's so medical, but its authors are medically oriented and so I can't fault them. I have never before, however, found a real description of an orgasm. I understand there are women who don't know whether they're orgasmic or not because they don't know what it is supposed to feel like. (There we go with those old "supposed to" lines again.) Therefore, I would like to give the medical description of an orgasm, and would like forthwith to endorse it as the most accurate I have found in any research book.

The book was written by Georgia Kline-Graber and her husband, Benjamin Graber. She is a registered nurse, he, a practicing physician. I will give them both one enormous "hurrah!" for many of the things they have come out in favor of, many of the myths they have successfully exploded, and for their general sympathy for women who are left, as they put it, "with instructions to 'relax and do what comes naturally.'" That's not a hell of a lot of help if you are, as one of my own doctor's patients was, a wife who had never been screwed in three years of marriage but didn't know because she didn't know how it was supposed to feel.

By the same token, I'd like to congratulate the Grabers for their interesting perspective on real orgasm as opposed to women's simply "playing back" the words they've been told are what an orgasm is *supposed* to be.

In my mind, and according to all of my interviewees, an orgasm is something so ephemeral as to be almost indescribable, with variations that will go on as long as does life. Therefore, the Grabers have done wonders with their following graphic description, which goes thus:

". . . the orgasm itself always occurs *inside the body*, in the vagina, or more precisely in the pubococcygeus muscle." [That's the inner lining of that levator sling.] "The contractions of this muscle . . . are identical to the ones that occur in male orgasm, which result in ejaculation, the spurting of fluid containing sperm. The muscular contractions are the hallmark of orgasm—male or female—and occur regardless of how the orgasm is initiated . . . without them *there has been no orgasm*."

But then the Grabers go on to say what I have always argued and never, until now, been able to prove medically. And that is that there are vast ". . . differences in the way the orgasm and vaginal contractions feel, *depending on whether or not something is inserted in the vagina. . . .*" [Emphasis added.] And that something should be a man. I have never forgotten a passage in the autobiography of Andy Warhol's superstar "Viva," wherein someone—I don't know whether it was the writer or not—went on to say that even with a vibrator, an orgasm felt so empty without a man.

That passage certainly struck a nerve in me, and I feel very strongly that most men have no idea just how important they are to women. Sure—orgasm is orgasm is orgasm—but it isn't Super Sex without a man bringing it on, penis inserted in vagina. That's the way Mother Nature arranged it. "Empty" is a rotten feeling, no matter how much one likes orgasms, and while you know I endorse them, however you go about getting them (and the more the better), I still believe in sex. Super Sex with a partner.

The Grabers go on to say that when something is inserted within the vagina there are both emotional and physical differences.

"When a woman receives . . . direct clitoral stimulation, she experiences very pleasant tingling sensations that slowly build up to orgasm. As she nears orgasm, the tingling sensations become more and more intense. As orgasm becomes imminent, her attention is focused on what is happening with her body. All other sensations—sounds, tastes, smells, etc.—are diminished." Didn't I tell you?

"The first distinct stage or step of the actual orgasm is a feeling of stoppage or suspension. It lasts only an instant and is quickly followed by the second stage; the sensations in the clitoris disappear and are superseded by a feeling of warmth and tingling through the entire pelvis (even though it is the clitoris that is receiving direct stimulation) and sometimes, with a really intense orgasm, in other parts of the body as well. The pelvis becomes flooded with a warm, heavy, sexual sensation which then becomes the most distinct feeling taking over from the sensations in the clitoris alone. In reality this feeling lasts for only about five seconds, but it seems much longer. Often there is a feeling of almost floating, and one is unaware of touching anything, such as a blanket or a pillow. Attention is riveted on experiencing the sensation, and outside distractions are easily ignored.

"The last stage occurs after a split-second pause following the feelings described above. Automatically, the pubococcygeus muscle contracts strongly, bringing the sides of the vagina together. With this contraction of the muscle, there is the same delicious feeling described above. As the muscle relaxes, the feeling stops, but the motion of the muscle relaxing or opening is felt as a movement. . . .

"An average orgasm will consist of three or four contractions; an intense orgasm can contain up to about fifteen contractions.

"If a woman experiences a continuous sensation of warmth and tingling but not the contractions, she is not having an orgasm, although she is quite close. The sensations of warmth and tingling before the contractions are a pre-orgasmic phenomenon and are equivalent to the 'ejaculatory inevitability period' in a man. (This is the point just before ejaculation occurs and is a sensation that most men can identify.)"

I don't want you reading these marvelous accurate descriptions of something that is almost indescribable and then getting worried about whether or not your contractions are exactly as described. *Please relax!* They will be your own, but at least you will know what an orgasm feels like—told in words more medically experienced than my own. I know what my own orgasms feel like; I know that sometimes (rarely) I can't make them happen. It doesn't worry me in the slightest, though it may irritate me perhaps, but I am secure in knowing that every single woman in the world can be orgasmic.

Who knows? Maybe you've been having perfect orgasms all along, but, like the patient who didn't know what to feel, you didn't realize it.

Now you have the Grabers' description of what an orgasm is and does to your body.

The Grabers, bless them, have gone one step further and laid it out for all the world to read and believe (at last) *that there is indeed a difference between clitoral and vaginal orgasms*. When I mentioned this fact to a friend, she said, "Well, *I* could have told anybody that!" So, probably, could any woman who has enjoyed Super Sex, but then the medical profession is often hard to convince, and so for years they have insisted that vaginal orgasms were nothing more than the action of the penis rubbing against the clitoris; that the interior of the vagina has few nerve endings (it's true) and therefore vaginal orgasm was literally an impossibility. Don't tell that to me!

The Grabers go on to explain that orgasm with intercourse has some pretty important differences from any other sort of orgasm. (And how! The main difference is the man.) As they say, when a woman is having intercourse she experiences most of the feelings *in the vaginal area*, not in the clitoris, if, as they put it, she is moving (remember that, ladies!). As they say, the clitoris gets *indirect* stimulation, but nothing compared to the stimulation to a filled (by a penis, I hope) vagina.

Though it's true that the walls of the vagina itself have few nerve endings (although any woman who's had Super Sex will question that fact), the pubococcygeus muscle, however—the muscle that is closest to the vaginal wall—is, as they put it, "replete with nerve endings." And they go on to say that if that muscle is *in good condition*—and the italics are mine—it is more likely there will be a sufficient amount of sensation for orgasm to occur.

When you have read the chapter on internal exercises, get on with them. The Oriental cultures know all about the value of a vagina that can do what you want it to do and squeeze whatever is in it whenever you feel like it. Ask any man whether or not he finds it pleasurable to feel the vagina closing in heavy contractions around his penis. I can promise you it is always a super experience for any man and guaranteed to bring on his own super orgasm. I doubt seriously that either partner will ask "Did you come?"

My own initiation into orgasm was, as I imagine it is with many women, accidental. I won't go into details except to say that it must have been the combination of some pretty heavily pent-up sexual drive with an accidental (I'll swear) pressure against my clitoris. I hadn't caught on to masturbation as yet. Bang! I almost flew across the room. I really didn't know what had happened to me but I certainly knew that something had, and that it was something I wanted more of. You know where that leads, of course.

The odd thing is, I would place my age at around eighteen. Late bloomer. But what's even more odd is that I wasn't sexually innocent. In my growing-up years, nice girls didn't "go all the way." They did everything else imaginable, however, sending the poor boy home to do God-knows-what for relief. I don't think the girls of my era cared. We petted a lot and that was that.

I didn't lose my own virginity until I was twenty-one. So there, all you doubters. And that was with a man with whom I was deeply in love. Fortunately, he had been married, he knew all about life and love (and sex), having lost his own virginity, he claimed, at age ten! I believe him, too. In any case, the first experience was frightening but pleasurable. But fear of pregnancy made me incapable of anything except wondering what would happen when I had to tell my family.

Even then, it was quite awhile before I discovered, one balmy beach-night, full moon and all, that it was *more* pleasurable if I moved too. I remember, as if it were yesterday, asking, "Why didn't you tell me?" No reply. He was busy.

I became a later and later bloomer, for there were other lovers, but, as I have described, I was simply too naïve and too stupid to deal with birth control. Therefore I lived in a state of panic about abortion and its horrors—we were still in the era when "nice girls didn't do that." (Nice girls did . . . I just didn't know it.)

And so I made do with an imaginative variety of things such as mutual masturbation, withdrawal (cruel, when I think of it), using condoms (not me, him) and still shivered with fear of pregnancy, never once thinking of consulting my physician for advice. Somehow, within the framework of all these machinations, I managed to hang on to the same lover for a period of nine years! And so I can only assume I was doing something right. Surely the man wasn't *that* masochistic! He definitely deserved better, however, because he taught me some wondrous things. He was a man totally relaxed about sex, totally content to take what was good, no matter how odd the birth-control methods. I truly feel apologetic to him these days—for his getting the short end of something.

But I will never forget that once, when I found orgasm hard-coming, this man said to me, "Think dirty thoughts." I laughed at the time, but I began to fantasize, and the stories he had in his head helped a lot.

"Thinking dirty" (meaning thinking sexy) can bring on that orgasm when it is imminent but not easy. Don't fear fantasies. They can be wonderful.

I think sexual maturity finally struck once I'd gotten rid of the ignorance that definitely did not bring bliss. That is when I finally learned to relax—there we go with that word again—and it is, beyond doubt, the key to Super Sex for both sexes.

There was one big hangup, however. At first I couldn't have a vaginal orgasm. I was horrified, having been one of those lucky women who *always* had multiplied-by-multiple orgasms. This time I got smart. I consulted my doctor. Know what he said? "Relax. One day you'll be pleasantly surprised." I did and—need I go on?

My sex life has been super ever since, and I am on my knees, as usual, to my super physician. In the course of interviews for this book, I mentioned this bit of advice to various gynecologists. All said, "You have a very wise doctor." I do. Now you do too.

The Myth of the Must-Be-Mutual Orgasm

Mutual orgasm is terrific. Ask anyone who's experienced it. But by the same token, ask plenty of people who have never experienced it and you'll find, I'll wager, a lot of sexually satisfied folk. For the mutual orgasm myth is one that has destroyed more than it's built, and I hope to expose it for the phantom it is.

And so now we come to the selfish syndrome. *Be* selfish about sex. If You're (capital You) experiencing a phenomenal orgasm, do you think for one solitary moment it isn't going to set off a reaction in your partner? If you think it won't, think again. For Super Sex is a circular experience—one partner's actions and reactions get the same thing going in the other partner with the end result—Super!

I've just been told by a worldly-wise male friend that there should be a word to less worldly-wise men here: If a woman has not had an orgasm but says she's satisfied, *please believe her*! I will echo that. Believe *me*, I have had some perfectly beautiful sexual experiences where orgasm just didn't happen for whatever reason (tired? feeling cuddly only? who knows?) but the feelings of sexual satisfaction were—well, I can only repeat—satisfying for me at that moment in time. Lord knows, I wouldn't want a life without orgasms, and I am lucky enough to know my partner well enough so that mutual orgasm is pretty common with us. But not always, by any means, and I couldn't care less, nor could he. (He told me so, that's how I know.)

It all comes right around to what the Grabers said to us in *Woman's Orgasm* . . . that a woman can be fulfilled as long as she is fully filled by a man. For you men who care about such, this does not refer to penis size. For us women it refers to the wonder of being filled by a wonderful man.

Eventually orgasm, perhaps even mutual orgasm, is bound to follow. And one usually leads to more. But if it *never* happens and you're sexually satisfied—then that's all that matters.

Sexual Feedback—
Loud and Clear

I've heard people say, "I think it's simply *disgusting* for people to make so much noise during intercourse!" That's their opinion. In my own, it's the primal sexual scream. I don't think for a moment you should be holding back on your emotions while you're enjoying Super Sex. If it's so super it makes you yell, then make sure (in case you're modest, which I'm not) your walls are thick. But as for holding back on anything—just forget it!

I had a little discussion one day with a co-worker who said, "How on earth did people make it before today's liberated crowd felt free to say what they want?" She had a good point. For as she said, "How can the other fellow know what you want if you don't tell him or her?" How indeed?

I think there's nothing more important to Super Sex than sexual communication, and neither party should feel the slightest bit shy about coming right out and saying what pleases him/her. It's the only way. It may be you've been holding back on something that would have been your partner's greatest pleasure all along. That's simply silly. Talk. You'll find out a lot about each other's fantasies, and chances are they'll jibe. Then think of the fun you can have acting them out.

As for the sexual scream, I cannot think of a more satisfying sound from the vantage point of a lover. I like to know when I'm pleasing my partner, and if there's total silence, sometimes I'm left wondering. Not so good for the ego, that, and likely to make one a bit tentative about any sexual experimentation. So let it all out every time you feel like it. You have nothing to lose but a neighbor, perhaps, and who cares about them?

In any case, as far as I'm concerned, that classic question, "Did you come?" should now be gone with the centuries. There should be no question about it.

Ignorance Is Not Bliss

Who am I to sit here and call anyone ignorant? And yet, after a recent visit to my own physician, I found that sexual ignorance is a great deal more prevalent than it ought to be. Happily, I have a doctor I can talk to. "With" would be a better word. He tells it like it is but is not out to embarrass—only to instruct.

I like that, for I want my answers flat-out honest.

He told me some amazing tales of non-wisdom that astonished me, and, he says, astonished him. I feel they should be passed along, just in case any of you might feel that everybody knows everything. And, by the way, just because you don't know everything is no reason to be embarrassed. The whole idea is to make sure you have no hangups about *telling* your problems to your doctor. If your doctor is the sort who can't cope with problems, then tell them to another doctor. I have found that gynecologists are often the most reluctant of all doctors when it comes to discussing sex. Is it their shyness that sent them on the route to gynecology? Have they sexual hangups of their own?

By the same token, gynecologists complain that their patients are often too shy to be honest with *them* and go on to say that it's rather difficult to treat something when the doctor doesn't know what that something is. I have been told such tales, for instance, of gynecologists' being asked to put patients through years (literally) of painful and exhaustive (as well as exhausting) tests to determine why they seemed unable to have children, only to discover that one damned good reason was that they weren't having intercourse! Perhaps they still believed babies were found in cabbage patches. The ignorance surrounding sex, both within the medical profession as well as without, is not only astonishing but appalling.

My own doctor tells me how shocked he was when he first started practicing medicine. Seems he was giving a patient a routine gynecological checkup, only to find, to his horror—and he knew this lady was married—that her hymen had never been broken. Meaning she was technically a virgin—a rarity these days, but particularly so among married women, I hope. My doctor says he retreated, and immediately asked the married lady to step into his office for a little chat. Apparently—and both he and I find this too difficult to accept, but it is true—the patient didn't know she had never been penetrated by her husband's penis because she didn't know how it should feel! I have no idea why the husband didn't figure out something was wrong, but, as it turned out, this particular woman had what is known as a fibrotic hymen—the sort that is so tough it must be opened surgically. Fortunately that condition is rare indeed. In fact, the condition is rarer than the married couples who do not have intercourse and seemingly don't even guess that something might be amiss.

I am astonished and dismayed. It's hard to talk about Super Sex to someone who doesn't know the fundamentals, but try I will. I never give up when I know that something as wonderful as wonderful sex can, and will, be accomplished by every determined reader of this book. And, while there may be a few folk about who don't care about sex at all, I will have to say that I have never found them. A friend once said to me, when I was speculating on the sex life of a rather asexual acquaintance, "Oh, come on, Mary Ann! *Everybody* does *something*, even if it's only with a doorknob!" Well, I've been pondering that doorknob statement for twenty years now and haven't figured out just how anyone would do it (perhaps this man knew) but then doorknobs don't turn me on. Let's get back to ignorance.

A physician told me that his wife didn't know where her vagina was until they were married. I hope the shock didn't show on my face. Perhaps it did, for he asked me, "How many women do you know who go about sticking their fingers up their vaginas?"

I must confess to not asking many women that question, but I cannot understand how a woman who has reached marriageable age could not know *something* about her own anatomy. If she uses tampons, or a diaphragm, then it is 100 percent certain she has to know how to find her vagina.

My own doctor tells me of a wonderful woman gynecologist—unfortunately now retired—who was asked by a patient during an examination, "Where is my clitoris?" At which point, gynecologist asked lady patient whether or not she carried a hand mirror. Patient got mirror from her purse and doctor shoved it into proper perspective and said, "There! That's your clitoris." Which is about the best way I can think of to find out.

I am not going to rave on about the magnificence of female genitals. I don't happen to think they're particularly gorgeous, much preferring the aesthetic quality of male genitalia, which is on the outside just waiting to be seen. And I certainly don't spend any time with a mirror looking at my own, but I do believe that somewhere back in my childhood, I developed a rash, or an itch, or (and this I do remember well) rubbed myself raw by riding horseback in tight jeans. You can bet I got a hand mirror and had a look, the better to be able to tell my doctor what had happened and get whatever relief I needed.

If you don't know where your vulva, your clitoris, your vagina are located, then for God's sake, ask your doctor. He isn't going to faint, and if he does, then get another doctor. Also, since this seems to be a prevalent kind of—not ignorance—let's call it innocence, don't be ashamed to ask.

I confess to being backward myself. I was well into my twenties before I had the nerve to request a diaphragm. The Lord was obviously on my side, since I didn't turn up pregnant, but I can tell you that I spent many a sleepless night worrying, and, besides that, my sex life was definitely affected by fear of pregnancy. I repeat, condoms, or male contraceptives, never seemed trustworthy to me, and there was no way any man could convince me they were secure.

Stupid me. Contraception is so simple, and sure beats such vicious measures as abortion, which can carry with it not only pain but heartbreak, guilt, and all sorts of other problems. Here is one time when that "ounce of prevention" is worth everything.

I will confess, however, that once I had decided to request a fitting for a diaphragm (and here I should tell you that I am afraid of The

Pill . . . with good reason, too. More later.), I dashed up to my long-time gynecologist and just requested. At which point, he blushed and refused. What did I tell you about gynecologists? This particular doctor is one of my favorite people in the world, and he isn't old, but he has old-fashioned ideas about unmarried women, apparently. Would he have preferred that I be impregnated?

I went to another gynecologist. Not the one my doctor wanted, since that one was away. This doctor fitted me with a diaphragm and sent me on my way. The only thing he forgot to show me was how to get it in and out. And, once more, I pulled a dumb act by not insisting he do so.

However, he had given me enough verbal instruction on how to get it in so that, next sexual session, I managed. And then, guess what? I almost never got it out again! Need I mention my panic? Fortunately, my own doctor's nurses don't take off the entire month of August (my doctor does, and now *he* was away), and so I rushed up to see the nurse who had helped care for me for most of my adult life. She was furious! She said she couldn't imagine such lack of concern with showing me how (P.S.—she did), and besides, if I was having so much trouble extricating the thing, it had to be the wrong size. Swell! Too small means not too safe.

This sensible nurse promptly got on the phone to the doctor we'd all wanted in the first place (finally back from vacation), and made an appointment for him to see me *immediately*, explaining my ludicrous predicament.

This time I got the right doctor. Sure enough, the diaphragm I had been given was too small. (If you have one at all, be sure to have the size checked at regular intervals, meaning once a year or so. Your vagina size changes with changes in sexual activity, so better safe than sorry. Cliché, so what?) Once my wonderful un-shy and totally sensible new gynecologist had determined the right size, he *showed* me how to insert the diaphragm properly, explaining that it simply wasn't in unless I could feel it slip behind the pelvic bone. And, he informed me, the pelvic bone is impossible to confuse with anything else, as it's the bone one feels with the finger (yes, some women have reason to put their fingers in their vaginas) when one inserts the diaphragm. It is the bone to the front, and you can feel it from the outside too. He showed me how to hold the diaphragm folded, push it inside the vagina, past that bone, and then release it. And then he left me. He said, "Stay here, put it in and take it out until I come back." Which was about twenty minutes later. I can promise you that by then, there wasn't much I didn't know about a diaphragm, and I used mine happily until it disintegrated. True. Don't let it happen to you. The thing looked in perfect shape to me until I extracted it one day and there was nothing left but the rim. Something tells me I'm not very fertile, which is certainly fortunate for me and my man. The point is, it should be replaced according to the instructions of the manufacturer whether it looks in fine shape to you or not. I am keeping mine as a sort of "soft sculpture." It has too many magnificent memories connected with it. You'll be happy to hear, however, that it isn't displayed on my coffee table.

I am not sure exactly why I have told you the intimate details of my goings and comings with gynecologists in order to achieve birth control except to show that there _is_ ignorance with probably all of us and with plenty of non-understanding doctors as well. Many physicians assume a lot of knowledge on the part of the patient that they should not. The point is, that if you _don't_ know, don't be embarrassed to ask, and if your doctor is embarrassed, then, I'll repeat, search out a different sort of doctor.

I have spoken at length about diaphragms because that happens to be, for me, the easiest possible method of birth control. And, unless your religion forbids it, birth control is a great step toward the relaxation you need for Super Sex. If you are fearful—as I was—you can actually experience pain during intercourse. The expression "up tight" applies literally here, and a woman can believe there is something physically wrong with her, when, in fact, fear is making her tighten up the muscles surrounding her vagina so that no man can enter. It's a completely unconscious, self-protective reaction that can cause a lot of pain, both mental and physical, when both parties want to screw. The fact of not having to worry about unwanted pregnancies is one reason, doctors have found, that many women have increased sexual appetites after menopause. (Just make sure it really _has_ been menopause. I'm sure you've seen babies born to women in their fifties who thought they had no worries. Always check with your doctor to be sure your childbearing days are over. In fact, always check with your doctor about everything.)

There are, of course, plenty of other methods of birth control available to women these days. There is The Pill, which is supposedly responsible for the sexual revolution of this era. It is also responsible for a few more things, and more and more doctors are looking upon it with wary eyes.

I had my go at The Pill, and I was lucky to escape with my life. Before my diaphragm days, I summoned the courage to ask my doctor about The Pill. He said, "I've been wanting to suggest that for years but didn't feel I should." Why shouldn't he? He's my doctor, after all, and there's nothing he doesn't know about me. (Which goes to show how reticent doctor and patient can be on the subject of sex.) That was some ten years ago, however, and now there is absolutely nothing I cannot discuss with him. We speak the same language, fortunately, and now there's no embarrassment about getting to any problem right away.

I went away with a prescription for that Pill and a certain degree of nervousness about it all. You see, I was born lucky. I have never had menstrual cramps in my life, and all of that part of me has been as normal as apple pie, regular as clockwork. Some small voice in me said it was a shame to start messing around with a body machine that was doing its job as well as mine.

Still, one day I summoned the courage to start the dosage. I don't like dosages of anything—especially if they are going to mess up something as important as one's hormones and, more especially, if there's nothing wrong with those hormones anyway.

Once again, I was ignorant. And stupid. I took The Pill. Now, all of my natural life I have suffered from vicious migraine headaches, like most of my family. They (meaning the medical profession) say that migraines can be hereditary, and in my case I imagine they are. But then the medical profession has a lot to learn about migraines, and give them credit—they're trying.

In any case, with a bit of nervousness I began my course of The Pill. In two days I was flat on my back with the most terrible migraine headache I have ever experienced—and that's something! Needless to say, I advised my doctor immediately, and he advised me to stop The Pill immediately. The Pill was stopped, but the headache wasn't. I was confined to my bed for two full weeks in complete agony. Once it was all over, and I was back to normal, there suddenly appeared in every newspaper (and don't think friends didn't send me clippings from all of them) that The Pill and migraine headaches (or, better said, migraine-headache-prone patients) mix to make cerebral hemorrhage. Lovely. I didn't even have a lover at the moment. Just the hopes of finding one soon. Can you imagine risking the possibilities of a stroke with its inherent chance of paralysis, just in case the right lover came along? Lot of good he could do then, even if you did live. Seems the fatality statistics are somewhere in the 90 percent bracket when you mix migraines with The Pill.

Forget it. It's the old-fashioned, easy, diaphragm way for me, and I do wish to warn anyone who has any reaction to anything at all to—I'll say it again—be honest with her doctor and make sure that he knows all the angles. You do, after all, want to save your life for a lifetime of Super Sex.

There are, of course, many other methods—or at least some other methods—of effective birth control. The IUD, or intrauterine device, is one. But one thing I must say. A friend of mine had one inserted and suffered the agonies of the damned until a second, more knowledgeable, physician removed it and damned the doctor who'd put it into the uterus of a woman who'd never had children. For some women, this, I understand, matters a great deal and there are many physicians who won't consider it. Others do it, and sometimes there's no problem, other times a great deal of pain at first. My advice is to get *good advice*, and preferably from several sources on this one—just as you would on surgery. The IUD isn't a toy, and your sex-health isn't to be toyed with.

By now I probably have you more nervous than relaxed. Certainly hope not, but I want you to be able to *really* relax, secure in the knowledge that you can make babies if and when you want them, but you can make love whenever you want. And I want that to be whenever the opportunity arises.

Too Much Knowledge Is a Dangerous Thing

My heroes, the Graber husband/ wife authors—they of the orgasmic description—have done one thing that I consider wrong, and I most strongly advise you not to try it.

You see, sexual feedback is important—I have talked about that— and if you're doing everything according to Super Sex, then you should be getting more than enough feedback from your partner in the form of more and more Super Sex and more and more obvious indications that he/she is pleased, pleased, pleased.

But when we get down to being scientific about sex, the romanticism of it all is ruined. (Yes, I freely admit to being romantic and I think Super Sex is always romantic—though not necessarily to be confused with being "in love.")

The Grabers suggest that every woman rush right out and purchase an instrument known as a perineometer—a device that measures their orgasmic strength, or rather the strength of their vaginal contractions.

Well, I don't know about you other ladies out there, but I, for one, would prefer to remain in the dark about the mathematical measurements of orgasms and permit my partner's pleasure to be my only measure. Can you think of what it might do to a woman to find her contractions were zilch—zero? I am quite sure it would ruin a lot of potential Super Sex. Why test your contractions against anything other than your partner's penis? If he isn't feeling anything, you'll soon hear it from him, and you can practice longer and harder on your interior exercises. But until you hear a complaint, I suggest leaving your contractions just between the two of you.

It's Not What You've Got, It's the Way That You Use It!

Right here and now I want to dispel a few myths about what makes a terrific lay. All of the locker-room talk about penis sizes and how they matter for macho is, once and for all, to be laid to rest for what it is—just so much garbage: myths propagated by men to appease men. Myths that can wreck those who think they haven't got what it takes.

Well, gentlemen, have I got news for you! Before I hit you with the hard facts about penis size, let me tell you that in all of my years of interviewing, I have yet to find a woman who gave a damn about the size of her man's penis—assuming that he knew how to use it in the manner that pleased *her*. Much to the contrary. I wish I could tell you how many women have said to me "Why do men think it's so important to have a big penis? I think it hurts!"

Occasionally true, I might add, if, for example, the woman's on top and is small and the penis actually penetrates so far it is honestly uncomfortable for her. No Super Sex there—not when there's discomfort.

And, if a man tends to come on rough, and cares not how it's going over (or in) with his mate, then, once again, that mate might be wishing for a more normal-sized man.

And normal is not so spectacular—at least not when the penis is relaxed. I've heard many men shyly admit they believed they were small, when, in fact, they were perfectly normal.

Now the team of William Masters and Virginia Johnson have come up with the following documented revelations for all men to consider.

According to Masters and Johnson, what few men (or even women) realize is that the smaller the penis when unstimulated (or relaxed), *the larger it becomes when stimulated*! And they go on to say that penises, when erect, vary in length only about 20 percent *at the most*, although the size, when flaccid, may vary by as much as *200 percent*!

So all of those locker-room jokes can go by the boards. For all that some men would like to believe it, they're not that different from everyone else.

Naturally there are deformities that can occur in any part of the human anatomy, and obviously somewhere, someone may have a deformed penis. But we aren't talking about those. We're just talking about men whose egos may have suffered severe psychological damage by believing their penises are "too small."

However, if the above statistics don't reassure any such men, perhaps this (from Masters and Johnson) will. They say that even those discrepancies in size that do exist (minor discrepancies they are), and persist after erection, are relatively unimportant, since, during intercourse, the woman's vagina automatically adjusts to the size of what's inside.

And, in fact, the only time a woman is really able to judge what's going *in* is at the entry to the vagina. Once a penis is inserted—usually within a minute of that insertion—the difference in size is irrelevant —unless, as I have said, the female partner is on top and the penetration is actually painfully hitting against the uterine wall. This is what produces the painful condition known as honeymoon disease—cystitis, or an inflammation of the bladder. Any woman who's had it would prefer not to have it again. That's one good reason why enormous penises are not every woman's first choice. As Masters and Johnson say, many women may be psychologically turned on by the idea of a large penis, but I frankly would find these women to be too juvenile to attempt Super Sex. For Super Sex is the arrival of the supreme sexual moment, the continuance of a supreme, unequaled sexual life for the rest of your life, and should have nothing to do whatsoever with such things as being turned on by the likes of *Playgirl* centerfolds.

Most of the men I have known were average. I'll amend that. *All* of the men I have known were average save one, who was one of the super jocks and—wouldn't you know?—so interested in his own anatomy that he was one of the worst lovers I ever knew. He went quickly from my life (just as he went quickly from his wife's) and now I don't even remember his name. But the average guys who were superb lovers—*I remember!*

FOR THE LADIES

As for the ladies, just a small paragraph about size as applied to them. It seems that many women suffer terribly because they have learned to equate breast size with sexuality . . . society's conditioning doing its dirty work once more on the minds as well as the sex lives of those unlucky enough to fall for it.

Masters and Johnson say that women have been virtually traumatized by our culture's attitude towards breast size—just like the men and their penises.

Then this knowledgeable (Who can deny that?) team goes on to calm every worried woman by stating that there is *absolutely no relation between breast size and sexuality*!

So some men are "breast men" (all right—I know there's another term but I'm trying to remain ladylike) . . . *So what?* The point is that once you've learned how to screw in an *un*ladylike manner, I doubt seriously whether any man is going to be busy measuring your cup size. He will—or he damned well should be—much too busy simply enjoying the rush of pleasure he'll get from your own wily knowledge of Super Sex.

In Praise
of Older Lovers

I have never known a youth who was a super lover. Childish charm, yes; the voice of experience, no. Not even the body of experience.

In my own opinion, sex never gets to be super until it's been practiced for years. And so, it may be true that youth is wasted on the young. You young creatures, so beautiful, may hate me, but the fact is that you're going to be more beautiful, and far more adept at Super Sex when you've had time to practice and practice and practice, which, of course, will make you perfect.

There exists a wonderful little (in size, not importance) book called *In Praise of Older Women* by Stephen Vizinczey. Although it had rave reviews when it was published, I have yet to find another soul who's read it. Let me say here that it's a book not to be missed by any man or woman who dreams of ever having lovers. That means every man and woman alive.

In the very beginning of this supposedly fictitious book (I don't know if it's autobiographical but wish I did) by a supposed scholar named Andras Vajda there are some wonderful quotes from some other scholars—our own Benjamin Franklin, for one, who says, "In all your amours you should prefer old women to young ones . . . because they have greater knowledge of the world."

Amen.

The truth is that the sexual peak of a man comes somewhere in his late teens, while a woman reaches her ripe sexual potential in her thirties. No wonder that marriages between older women and younger men are listed as the happiest going.

But doesn't that leave our older women with younger, less experienced men? Yep. That doesn't mean that younger lovers can't be brought up to become experienced older-and-wiser ones.

As for myself—well, for many years, I always had younger men. That was before I met the super man I have now, and discovered that older is indeed wiser. It's a whole lot better that he did his practicing pre-me! Now we just get on with Super Sex, both wise in already acquired knowledge.

Author Gail Sheehy has done a book called *Passages* in which she considers in depth the differences between the sexes, sexually, at different points in life. It is, it seems, a physical fact that a man of fifty hasn't the erection-recuperation powers of a boy of eighteen, who can go on and on and on. But, as Ms. Sheehy says, "The bright side of the male sexual life cycle is this: a man in generally good health need never lose his erective capacity. The sexually educated and experienced middle-aged man can be a most satisfying lover. Once he overcomes the anxiety about no longer being a boy, he can begin to appreciate his matured powers to give tenderness, to receive love from an independent woman." Here's to Gail Sheehy! Give me a man with matured powers any night.

Boys are fun but men are men.

As for the men who want the babes-in-arms chicks . . . doesn't it, as Ms. Sheehy sees it, come from a flourishing fear of growing older? That's how I see it. And that's how a middle-aged man can make himself the object of some pretty heavy ridicule. Check the Beverly Hills Hotel on a Sunday morning for a lot of "uncles" having breakfast with their sexy Sunday "nieces." Most people laugh.

For you men in the throes of teen-age enchantment, I can only beg you to read my favorite book praising older women. The chapter "On Virgins" begins with a quote, "O purity, painful and pleading." Purity? Is *that* what you're after? Then why are you reading a book on Super Sex?

As far as I am concerned, with Super Sex it's, once again, not what you've got—in this case youth—but the way that you use it. Which is, I hope, in the case of older lovers, wisely and well.

The Strength to Go On and On—
Exercises to Give It

Being an older lover—or, even a younger one—does not mean you have the right to collapse at the wrong moment of Super Sex. Strength is ultimately important to the success of Super Sex, and everybody must be able to hang in there, hang on and be strong enough not to think about musculature at a Super Sexual moment.

From a woman's vantage point—and that's the only point from which I can write—these illustrations ought to give you a pretty good idea of what these exercises are getting at—or rather what I want *you* to be getting at.

These are good for pectoral strength, which, as Nicholas points out, you even need for a "bear hug."

This exercise strengthens the entire front of the body, and its purpose is pretty obvious to me. It strengthens the arms, chest, abdomen, hips, thighs, and legs, meaning you can keep at Super Sex for as long as you want if you can perform the exercise here. Warning: it is a toughy, so don't expect to do it this way at first. Once again, a damaged body is no good to *any*body, so go at it ever so gently in the beginning and, with time, you'll be able to do this (and everything else) to perfection.

This can be difficult, so watch out and simply do not expect to do it well at first—no one will expect you to. This exercise is meant to be a very gradual process to strengthen and increase your capacity for power—in everything. Just don't rush it. The results will begin to show immediately, however, and the more you progress with this one, the more it shows up in your Super Sex life.

In support position, with hands and feet flat on the floor, slowly separate your hands and feet to spread as wide as possible. Do this gradually, inch by inch.

When you are spread-eagled as much as possible, maintain the position from six to thirty-six seconds.

Breathe normally—the neatest and most important trick of all.

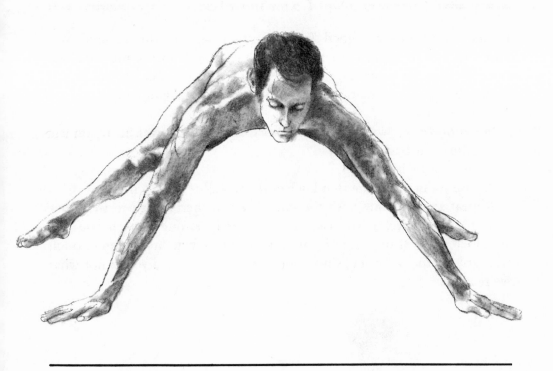

These exercises are good for strengthening the thighs—and you know what the thighs are good for. Nicholas informs me that the exercises also act as massage for the glands in the lower abdomen. I'll leave that bit of information between you men and Kounovsky.

Stand between two chairs for support, with your hands firmly on the top of the chair back.

Lunge back with one leg.

As you stand up, bring that knee of the straightened leg high.

Repeat several times with the same leg and then switch to the other leg. Or, if you prefer, you can alternate legs, as long as each one gets equal exercise. If one time is all you can muster at first, keep enough strength for the other leg, since, once again, a one-sided you is not what we're after.

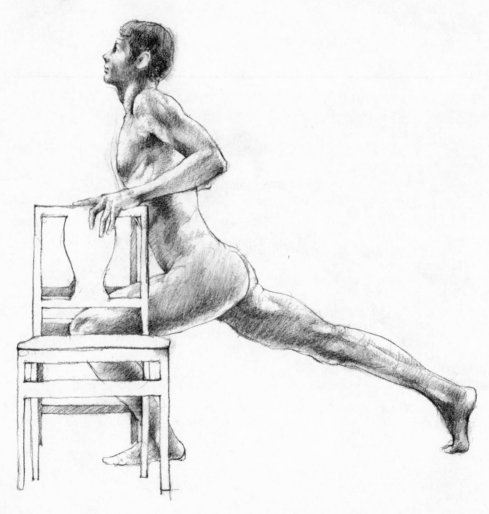

Using a chair, with the chair pushed against a wall to prevent its slipping (the illustration was done in the open for clarity), put your feet as far back as you can and try to do several push-ups. Kounovsky tells me that for some men it's more difficult to bring the feet closer to the chair—all depending on your height, etc. The point is, for results, make it as difficult as you can, but push down on the chair seat and *don't* try to show off. Perfection is what is wanted, even if it takes time, and time is what it may take, so slowly—remember?

For thighs, hips, and abdomen: sit on the edge of the chair, with your hands holding the seat on either side.

Bend one knee after the other *slowly and completely*. Exhale as you compress (bend) your knee, inhale as you extend it.

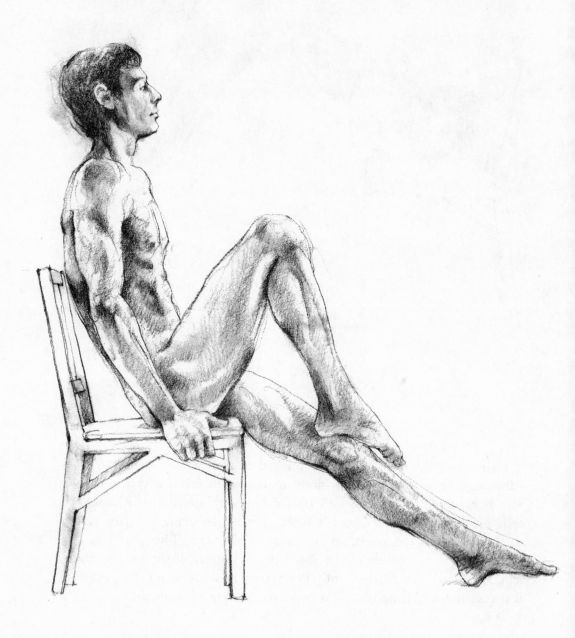

Sitting on the floor, with your feet up (legs straight) on the seat of the chair, put your arms forward and try (just try) to touch your toes while you contract your abdomen and your thighs at the same time. Exhale on the way to your toes, inhale coming back up. Believe me, the exhalation makes the chest smaller and therefore makes getting to your toes easier! Nicholas Kounovsky tells me that this one should appeal to every man's vanity since it works on the abdominal girdle, meaning you'll never need to wear one!

For those of you who have never tried such exercises, Kounovsky suggests you put your hands behind you on the floor, feet up on the chair, and then try to sit for a few seconds without the aid of your hands. Your stomach, waistline, and abdominal girdle will all feel what you are doing.

In the same sitting position, feet on the chair, and arms outstretched, twist your torso to the left, trying to touch your feet with your *right* hand.

Then reverse, twisting to the right and trying to touch the feet with your left hand.

Always exhale when you reach for your feet, inhale when you reverse positions.

The Sweet Smell of Success

I have just finished reading a most fascinating diatribe on things meant to take away the sweet smell of female. Or the sweet smell of sex. Or the sweet smell of successful sex. (Even that irreplaceable smell of male.) I shall quote some of it to you shortly because, thank God, someone finally said it for anything that deodorizes all of the *you* out of you!

All of my life I have believed—and now, as is often the case, science is not far behind the layman—that smell just may be the elusive magnet that attracts one person to the other. And equally repels others. Have you never known someone who smelled sweet but not your sort of sweet? Think about it.

In any case, the marvelous piece on, as she puts it, "Dealing with the, uh, Problem," came from Nora Ephron's wonderfully flat-out and honest book called *Crazy Salad*. It is rare when one author wants to write fan letters to another. There is a touch of jealousy in the breed. But I have read so many really *good* books that helped me say what I have to say that after this, I may become a letter-writer after all.

Nora Ephron writes about the business of feminine-hygiene sprays. And if you think it isn't big business then consider that Alberto-Culver, according to Ms. Ephron, has managed to add $40,000,000— that's right, forty *million* dollars—onto their gross volume with one product alone, and that product is something meant to take the female out of your female organs.

And, naturally, Alberto-Culver is only one of many manufacturers, proving that would-be-fascinating women are falling for the old advertising con game once again. (I'm not, but that's because I've been out alone in the business world too long.)

According to Ms. Ephron, "American women are pushovers for this product." Actually, Dr. Norman Pleshette, a New York gynecologist, said that, and is quoted further as saying, "I think it comes down to menstruation, which many are taught is unclean." Dr. Sheldon Cherry adds that feminine-deodorant sprays simply capitalize on the fears and sensitivities women have about odor "down there."

Dr. Cherry points out the obvious. No woman should need a vaginal deodorant. And if she does—if she really and truly is odoriferous—then she should pay her gynecologist a visit *fast*. If she just smells like a woman, then swell.

As Ms. Ephron says, the fascinating paradox is that, in the midst of the so-called sexual revolution, manufacturers of cosmetic products are able to capitalize on the implicit message that sex is dirty and smelly.

Don't think men have escaped. There are crotch sprays for them as well. And, for the men who think they don't have their own (sweet to me) individual odors—let them be aware. A man's pubic hair smells like a man's pubic hair. It is individual, and it is nice. It is not dirty unless *he* is dirty, in which case (in my case) he can leave on the run.

The people who manufacture these products actually have human guinea pigs who are willing to lie, half sheet-covered, on a table to be submitted to the "sniff test." Ye gods! I cannot imagine what the sex lives of this country could come to if the advertising world always got its way. And, in this case, they (sadly) seem to be getting it.

In this same chapter, we are provided with the incredible tidbit about a tape-recorded housewife session (provided of course, by a market research firm) wherein one woman said: "I think the new deodorant sprays are sensational . . . the sprays eliminate having to touch yourself."

In short, everything I am trying to teach you *not* to think, this woman had firmly implanted in her brain by someone, somewhere, sometime.

Ms. Ephron's piece goes on to quote a New York psychoanalyst as saying that one of the first signs of real paranoia is the feeling that one smells bad. If you have no other reason to believe me, that should do it.

But stop for a moment to consider that all these de-personalizing deodorizers can be, and often are, dangerous.

They can cause burning and itching in the vulvar area (that's the part of you that protects your vagina, for those who still haven't got hold of a mirror). The clitoris is often swollen and remains peculiarly abnormal. Some gynecologists say that the condition of irritation to the vulva disappeared the moment the sprays were discontinued.

And doctors say that men had best watch for the same symptoms from their "down there," if they're busily spraying their penises.

The truth is that the human body is uniquely put together. It seems to know what to do for itself, if only we will let it. The vagina, for example, is equipped to deal with the normal things that enter it . . . such as unsprayed penises. Like the rest of the body, the interior of the vagina is blessed with a slight acidity that makes it normally clean, normally infection-resistant, normally odor-free.

But, just to show what the general American attitude on "down there" is, I turn to one more book to which I cheerfully take off my author's hat. That book is called *The First Time* and was written by a husband/wife team, Karl and Anne Taylor Fleming.

Here's a book that every one of you out there—doctor, lawyer, merchant chief—*must* read, because it gives a pretty magnificent insight into what isn't the so magnificent sex life of many a so-called swinger.

The part that applies here comes from that self-styled femme-fatalizer, Bobby Riggs, who goes on to say that in his youth "Guys who would eat pussy, they were terrible or queer or something. And nobody would admit it if they did. There were all those old wives' tales about it and how could anyone think of putting their tongue on that, like your tongue might fall off or something." But then, now-mature, twice-married Bobby tells us that he's gotten to the point (at age fifty-seven, or so) of thinking it's part of the game, and that if you like a person and have a feeling for them there's nothing at all wrong with it. Gee, Mr. Riggs, I'm delighted to hear you've discovered what 91 percent of the 1975 *Redbook*-surveyed women have apparently known for some time. Oral sex is part of Super Sex. But you know what

Bobby says? "If you can get over the smell, you have it half licked." I wonder just how he meant that! Or is Bobby still a sexual baby?

Since Ms. Ephron wrote her magnificent put-down of the vaginal-spray industry and its deliberate "taking" of the American woman, we've moved on to the douche crowd, who advocate washing the vagina regularly with some substance—generally one with a sticky-sweet name, clearly indicating disapproval of the normal female odor—that is sup-posed to make you clean (you are), sweet-smelling (you are) and possibly even fruit-flavored. Once again, I say "rot" to all that. If you use such douches, you may be the one to rot, for I understand from gynecologists in the know that such products are just as harmful as the crotch sprays. In fact, any gynecologist worth his M.D. will happily tell you that douching is never needed unless there is infection or some other gyne-cological problem present—in which case he will prescribe a proper product. Therefore, believe in your womanhood and forget about strawberry-scented underpants. If a man is after that, he can always go out for a soda!

Remember, for your sake. You smell like you. And that's good. All over.

Nobody Needs
First Aid

Something in the back of my head has always told me that those who are continually after something new and kinky may just be a little bit bored with sex. Which to my mind means that they don't know enough about just how Super Sex is supposed to be.

Super Sex is super. Super Sex is superior. Super Sex is magnificent. Super Sex wipes out everything else one might sense, leaving only the sensation of its shattering emotional and physical release. When one is experiencing Super Sex, the world disappears and every emotion is concentrated on the sexual enjoyment of it all. That is why Super Sex should not be fragmented. That is why I am going to come out now and say a few negative things that may make some of you hate me for a time . . . but only those of you who are beginning this book in the middle. And that should be nobody.

For now I have shown you how to achieve Super Sex—how to feel what you may never have felt before, known what you never knew yourself to be capable of.

Those who have done as I said, and learned the lessons first, can read this chapter knowing that it isn't for them anyway. But for others —the ones who haven't practiced enough—well, I am going to come right out and say everything negative I can think of about any *un-*

natural aids to Super Sex. *You don't need them!* Furthermore, they are distracting, and any distraction from the action at hand (?) is what you *do not want*.

I will start with group sex. Frankly, I don't dig it. How could I? I've never tried it and never will because I believe that group sex is for those who never had Super Sex, or are bored by sex itself and think that they may find some kinky kick by adding bodies. In truth, it can only make Super Sex impossible. I can promise you that when you have reached the ecstatic orgasm of Super Sex, one more body in bed is exactly what you don't want. Don't worry. I'm not so square that a lot of my friends don't invite me to orgies, but they always admit they aren't much fun and always end up in one-to-one situations anyway with everyone looking embarrassed indeed. Sorry. I'll take my own super man *alone,* and heaven help the man or woman who tries to have him with me!

I can't resist quoting from Bernie Cornfeld—simply because of his "ladies' man" reputation. In *The First Time* he says about orgies: "I've never been into orgies. I find them unromantic. [Author repeats —take the emotion out of sex and you ain't got Super Sex.] One of the girls described an orgy as where somebody is always shoving their or somebody else's fingers up your ass. That's why she stays clear of them, and I can understand that point of view." Me too, Bernie, and *bravo!*

As for other unnatural supposed uppers, let me be equally down. Starting with alcohol. Alcohol is an aphrodisiac all right, because it's a bladder irritant. It also suppresses some of the ego, allowing the id, with its often-accompanying guilts, to surface. Now why anyone on earth would feel guilty about a better sex life will always remain a mystery to me, but then perhaps my views are rare. I like sex and I like it super. OK. Alcohol lets you loose and it may even excite you at first. After that, its continued use is the primary cause of the decline of sexual abilities. Regular use almost always results in impotence. Some super!

There are the seemingly innocuous so-called tranquilizers that are the darlings of America (59.3 *billion* prescriptions were written by physicians in 1975 alone) and are used to cure (their users believe) every mental ill, every stress and every fear. For those who fear sex, tranquilizers may seem the answer, along with booze, pot and all the rest. Remember one thing. All of those little pills are far from harmless. They can be addictive, they most certainly do not allow Super Sex to show itself and, worst of all, you could end up a "pillie." It's the same as a junkie, and never let anyone—including well-meaning doctors— say otherwise. Your health, which is imperative for your sexuality—is at stake. Take it from me. Super Sex is all anybody needs.

Also, of late, there's been an enormous amount of press coverage given to the effects of marijuana on sex. Good old Mary Jane. I thought she'd grown too old to be mentioned—or that everyone had discovered the drawbacks of potted sexual plans. Sure, it can relax you and make you feel good. It can also make you paranoid, drowsy, giggly and all manner of things, depending on whether you've gotten Colombian Red or Peruvian this or Acapulco that. Personally, I like to know what I'm doing from the moment I step into any sexual situation. And I mean *know*. As far as I am concerned you can get as potted as you want, but never when you want Super Sex, because Super Sex will never happen under those conditions. Anything that removes supreme concentration is going to remove your chances for the superstar happening of your sexual life. I don't want it going up in smoke. Just one medically proven aside: mucous membranes dry up from marijuana use, making intercourse often painful. I ask you . . . super? And as for the men . . . they're saying beware of impotence. For women's sake, please be aware.

Just when I thought I had done with warnings, a friend reminded me I'd forgotten "poppers." As he is another nonbeliever in the drugged-and-tranquil way of life, I am going to take his advice and advise you as well.

Poppers, which you all may know well, is just another name for amyl nitrate, and amyl nitrate just happens to be a drug that was never meant to be toyed with—certainly never meant to be abused as a sexual stimulant.

Like almost everything else useful when used properly, however, it *is* abused, by those least likely to know what lies in store. What lies in state might be their own bodies.

I have never forgotten that many years ago—light-years before the dawn of the flower-power drug subculture—my doctor (who is a very permissive man) and I were discussing pot. He allowed as how if I wanted to try it to see what it was about, I could do so. He himself was curious, but he realized what a patient might feel if, on an emergency call, he ended up with a spaced-out doctor. How wise this man is! And how I respect him for never letting curiosity get *that* cat!

But he said, "Whatever you do, there's one thing you must never try, and that's poppers." Never having even heard of them, I asked for, and got, a description of what poppers can do. According to my doctor, "They're a good way to get yourself killed." Enough said to me. I want to live. And live and live. Amyl nitrate is a drug used on coronary patients. Its primary purpose is to open—explosively—the valve of the heart, permitting a rush of blood to enter. And, of course, if you're not a heart patient in need of amyl nitrate, that sudden rush can simply wreck your heart. I can, off the top of my head, name about fifteen men under forty who've popped off on poppers and been found by worried friends days after their untimely deaths. And these are those *known* to me. Think of how many other unsuspecting fun-seekers find more than fun for their money.

When I quizzed my doctor as to exactly why anyone felt they needed poppers, he said they claimed to him they had better orgasms, but that his own personal theory was that they simply didn't have very good sex and were overreaching. Overkill. That's what can happen when you dabble in drugs. Don't.

Up Yours

efore anyone asks, I may as well tell you that when it comes to anal sex, I confess to being a chicken. It hurts.

Anal sex is perfectly acceptable to some people, and in many countries it is used as a sure-fire method of contraception, particularly among the uneducated.

According to the famous *Redbook* survey on sex, however, there aren't too many American women who *prefer* anal to vaginal sex.

There are definite connections, however, between the anus and the vaginal pleasure-giving sensors. Having one's anus stimulated by the partner's finger during intercourse or foreplay is often double-the-fun. On the other hand, some people freak out completely at the idea, considering that part of the body "dirty." Remember what I said about *no part of the body's* being "dirty" unless it is in fact dirty, meaning unwashed.

If you intend to make anal sex a part of your Super Sex life, and you are a woman, there is one very important thing to remember. Never go directly from anal to vaginal sex, on the long shot that your partner's penis may bring some unneeded germs into the vagina during the switch. This is one time when coitus should be interruptus. He must go and bathe it—and that's that!

Unfortunately, the vagina is not equipped with any normal protection from the sort of bacteria or whatever that could be lurking in your own anus. Infection is what you do not need or want.

Men, of course, have orgasms from anal sex. An entire population of homosexuals know that. However, I understand that any normal man produces a spontaneous erection when his prostate gland is manipulated—often to his embarrassment on a doctor's examining table.

Women have no such glands, and I cannot for the life of me find any doctor or anybody who can tell me whether or not women have orgasms from anal sex. Since I am too chicken to check this one out for you personally, then you will have to tell me. However, I would presume that the woman who enjoys anal sex does indeed reach the orgasmic state occasionally. I would also presume that it would have a lot more to do with her head than with her anus. Orgasms are highly psychological, as we certainly know by now. So, if it's OK for you, then do it.

One more thing for women to remember, though. The sphincter muscles around the anus are not accustomed to receiving anything as large as a penis. Tightening these muscles, perhaps in anticipation of pain, can indeed cause pain. Before trying anal sex on for size, be sure your partner lubricates his penis with something as innocuous as K-Y jelly. It has been suggested by doctors—who ought to know—that wearing a condom (a rubber, that is) is a good idea. The better to keep those germs out, my dear.

Let me know what it was like.

A Lesson
for Men Only

Aly Khan, the prince of lovers, once boasted that his success with women was due entirely to his knowledge of the ancient Eastern art of love known as *carezza*.

From what I, as a woman, know about what I have seen (and felt) of this technique (and you can call it what you will), it is precisely what every woman dreams of. Never let a woman tell you she doesn't.

It is the extreme concentration that allows a man to withhold ejaculation—and withhold and withhold and withhold—until the woman is literally crawling the walls with desire. Sound corny? Not if you're doing it. Aly Khan said it was his pride. I don't blame him.

Charlie Mingus (yes, the musician) gave a pretty good description of the right kind of loving in his book *Beneath the Underdog*. Mingus had a friend whose youthful-seeming father occasionally entertained the young boys with lessons in love. He told them sex was important and not meant to be dirty. (Right!) Learn to control yourself, he admonished. Find out about girls. . . . This is the whole art of sex between a man and a woman.

And Mingus goes on to relate the older man's (older lover's?) advice in almost too much detail for me to quote here without blushing. (Well, the book says Charlie blushed, so why can't I?)

The basic idea, however, was that "for those who don't have the natural talent, here are some good rules for fucking." And then: "Kiss her. Play with her awhile. Then insert your peppermint stick, just the knob, the head of it. Rub it all up her slit for a long time over the clitoris, in just a little bit and out, from bottom to top and around until she's warming up to you. You gonna make love like this for hours, kissing, playing, sucking her breasts and fingering that good pussy till she's begging for you. Then you don't just ram it in. You put the head in sorta gentle and easy."

I wish more men would remember *that*. I think I've said, and I'll repeat, that women consider any grabbing at them as an assault almost as bad as rape. It's psychological rape but has real, adverse effects.

The gentle, gentle and oh-so-slowly bit is the part that really snares the woman. Seduction, not assault. You men will find, as Mingus's mentor did, that most women will soon be begging for you.

But, as the Easterners believe, the true joy of Super Sex lies in the ability to make it last and last and last. They advocate intercourse with the man's concentrating on withholding his ejaculation, allowing the woman all the orgasms she wants. Then the man withdraws, talks, walks about, whatever, and the whole game begins again.

It sounds to me as if it could go on for days, and that sounds like some fun. But then days of Super Sex are perfect for me.

Mingus's father-figure advised, "Tease. Move every which way, but so easy she can barely feel it move. Tighten and loosen its muscles [apparently men are equipped to do interior exercises as well as women]. That gives her a throbbing sensation. She'll start reaching for it again. Pull away. Just when she gives up and settles on her ass, hit it in hard and deep as you can and draw it out fast and hit it quick again." And there is much, much more of such teasing and taking in this one man's guide to *carezza*. This particular old man bet Charles Mingus that if he tried it on the next girl he got, she would tell him these very words: "Charles, I never had it done to me like that in my life!"

I'll only say I'd like it done to me that way *all* my life, as would—I'll stake my all on it—every woman you know. Therefore, if you men can concentrate on holding in, giving pleasure and waiting to get it—thereby assuring the most super pleasure—you have learned the art of *carezza*, which is nothing more than super Super Sex.

Super-Sex
Secrets I Know

PARTICIPATION

There are some things so basic to the success of Super Sex that I felt they were obvious and considered not including them in this book. But then, sometimes, things are obvious to one, and perhaps not to another. In the course of my research I found, more and more to my surprise, that the basics often remained hidden subjects—whether from fear-to-ask or total-innocence.

In any case, I have decided that—basic or not—such things as how to achieve Super Sex in exactly X number of steps is a matter not to be taken lightly, never to be overlooked, and intended to be included in this book. So—if you've heard it before—bear with me. If not, who knows? Perhaps one of these clues will produce the Super Sex you may have been waiting for all of your life.

One thing I (and many other researchers) can vouch for is that men—more often than not—do a lot of complaining about the fact that some women "just lie there" waiting to get laid. What these men do themselves to make such a woman move I'm unable to say. (I *will* say that the beautiful burden is on them as much as on the women.) The incentive for a woman to move may indeed lie with a man's approach, for the wham-bam method won't make a sexpot partner out of any woman. Personally, if I were approached thus, I'd get the man out of me and out of my bed fast. When, in other chapters of this book, I've mentioned that active sex is the kind that's not only best, but best for you, I mean exactly that. *You move.* It isn't meant to be just anticipation, but participation. Men have to move if they're on top. Women have to move if *they're* on top. But women should be moving anyway. Ever since that balmy beach night when I discovered the pleasures of perpetual motion, I've been hedonistic enough to keep it that way. That's why we've been so busy putting all those pelvises into super shape. That pelvis is going to rotate—side to side, up and down, or in whatever direction you most acutely feel the hard penis within you. (That's for women. You men do the same with the same Super-Sexual result.) I will positively stake my life on the fact that the penis within is going to make it double the pleasure for that perpetual motion. That's the idea behind Super Sex. Double, triple, quadruple the pleasure you've ever experienced before. When you've managed that, you've just begun to enjoy Super Sex. When it all gets so good you can't remember much afterward—certainly not how you did it—then Super Sex is what you've achieved. Never, *never* lie like a sodden lump waiting to get what you assume is due you, or what you feel is your duty. (If *that's* your problem, either get thee to an analyst or get a different partner!) Sex is meant to be super for both parties. (I want no duty-doers among you men either. If you don't like what you're getting, speak up!) If, for some reason, it doesn't seem Super-Sex time on any particular night, then put it off. Better to waste a night than a lifetime of Super Sex.

FUCK GUILT!

Guilt does not belong in the coital bed. Why? Because sex is super, sex is beautiful, sex is normal, sex is natural, sex feels good, sex is good for you, and without it your life would be empty indeed. Where should guilt come into a beautiful picture like that? Please, I beg of you, try to cast aside everything you've ever been taught by well-meaning parents, etc., about nice girls/boys don't do such things. We all know our parents did. If you are in bed for the purpose of sex, the guilt gets left out. Unless it is left out, Super Sex will be impossible, and Super Sex is what I want you all to have. And what I will do my damndest to see that you are able to have for as long as you want, which will be, I hope, forever and ever.

THE MORE YOU GET, THE MORE YOU WANT

I shall never forget accusing a lover of mine—who seemed not so eager for me anymore—of getting his sexual satisfaction elsewhere. Later on, I found out he simply wasn't getting sex, period. I presume he had successfully sublimated his sexual drive by work, worry or whatever, but it surely wasn't showing up in bed. When we finally got back into our normal sexual swing, things were as swinging as when we first met eight years before (and, yes, I was beginning to believe his story that he was getting old!). You see, sex is circular—no two ways about it. The more you get it, the more you want it; and the more you want it, the more you get it. Someone once asked me, "Why is it that when I haven't any boy friends, none appears, and if I already have one, I am inundated with offers?" Because she's giving off sexual vibes, that's why, and that's what always happens. That's why I have advised you to masturbate if a partner's not present, to keep your mind (and body) turned on to sex, so that sex will turn up as regularly as it should in your life. And that should, and could, be every day, as far as I'm concerned. Some will cringe, but everyone's clockwork is different, so be your own judge. That's not my role. I'm simply here to remind you that if you forget about sex—even for a moment—you're out of the Super-Sex race. Stay in it!

THE TENDER TOUCH

I've talked a lot about fondling, but I wonder whether women realize how much touching can mean to a man. Do all women know that many men's nipples are as sensitive as their own? How many care to discover that manual stimulation—while other things are happening as well—of the anus can be a super turn-on? In fact, how many people communicate at all about their sexual fantasies—what turns them on as well as what is guaranteed to turn them off? I am not speaking of sexual aberrations, for those belong with a psychiatrist and not with me. I *am* talking about all of the things one thinks about in private but rarely passes along to one's mate. How's the mate to know? And you'd be surprised how often the fantasies jibe, and what fun it is when they do! But right now we're talking about touching, and touching is the very first turn-on to what may come later. Don't reel at the word "may." If, on any given night, one of you decides that, for some reason or other, tonight's *not* the night for Super Sex, then so what? You've gotten together, over a pair of bare bodies, you've touched and fondled and learned (I hope) a lot about what appeals to your partner. That will come in plenty handy when it's Super-Sex time. I have the sneaky suspicion that Super Sex—once those bodies are bared and fondled— will rear its beautiful head right then. Anybody for bets?

MOVE IT!

You women have been admonished to do your inner exercises for your own good. I'm not sure I've admonished you men enough. For the penis is one big muscle and should be able to flex and be as agile as any in-shape muscle should. Therefore, you, too, should practice. See if it will go this way and that at your command. Meanwhile, you women are learning to control your vaginas, closing and opening them at will (soon on the in-control penis inside). Imagine the Super Sex involved when two such muscles get together! Each movement from one is going to set off a related and superimposed motion in the other, making for some mighty steamy sex before it's all over—which could be a long, long while. So doing inner exercises when you're alone makes for Super Sex when you're together. I defy anyone who's experienced the phenomenon of "come together, right now, in me" to say it isn't super. This much I know.

ONCE ISN'T NECESSARILY ENOUGH

People, it seems, have odd—and not always correct—ideas about how long sexual intercourse should last. Given my way, I'd make it forever, except that by now I'd be long-gone dead and therefore unable to enjoy it. Nature, after all, built a certain amount of safety-valve wear-out factor into us—the better to save us for future Super Sex.

I believe, though, that we should establish, once and for all, the business about who has the multiple orgasms. First, I'll say that I believe *everyone*—properly taught and practiced—is orgasmic. And I believe that everyone who is orgasmic is multiple-orgasmic.

It came as a shock to me to learn that even men don't know much about men, because many seem to think that a man can't feel an orgasm more than once at a time. It is true that a man can only have two sequential ejaculations, since his scrotum contains only two sacs of semen. But his orgasms can go on and on. Once—and only once in my life—I kept count. Mostly from amazement. The superman involved got to eight! Nobody believes the story except the two of us, and I can assure you we weren't out to break records—simply enjoying Super Sex.

If a woman knows how to keep a man going (by her perpetual motion both inside and out), he will continue to climax and, depending on his lasting powers (which ought to be super by now), he can go on far past his ejaculation powers. After all, we aren't seeking impregnation but pleasure.

A woman is blessed with the ability to go on and on. You men out there should realize that often a woman is less able to turn off her sexuality, once she has had an orgasm, than she was before she took off her clothes. If she can go on, and wants to, and you can't, then for heaven's sake don't leave her unrelieved. Manipulate her manually. Orally. Hold her. *Ask* her what she wants. But let the good times roll until they stop.

THE SHAPE
OF SUPER SEX

The Shape of Super Sex

Terrific! That's what Super Sex looks like when it begins (in little time at all) to show in your shape. For sex—the very act of intercourse that gives so much pleasure to you, does everything for the psyche, cures the health hazards that beset us all—good old (no, new) Super Sex is the very thing that can give you the shapely shape you want, be you man or woman.

First of all we're going to give you all the lowdown on what makes that "terrific" into the shape (including the shape of your skin, the shape of your hair, the shape of *you*) that will get you the one and only partner you may have your sex-sights set on. While we're at it, we're going to have you practicing the exercises that will keep your shape in shape, while they're making your sexuality more obvious to all.

Don't kid yourselves, men. Your shape is important too. Let's just say it would be pretty darned embarrassing to have you give out just before a Super-Sexual climax. Your strength, agility and ability to go where you must, when you must, and for as long as you must are all part of what is going to make up your half of a Super Sexual couple.

And when it comes to such things as what is going to make you just plain healthy, hale and hearty—that applies to men and women alike (no sexism in health)—I hope and pray that both parts of a couple will look to the shape of Super Sex before they hope to attain it.

One more important reason for being in shape for Super Sex: it means that you're going to be in shape not only *for* Super Sex but for *attracting* Super Sex along with that Super Sexual man or woman meant just for you.

In short, you'll be putting your best looks forward, your good health will be the best side effect, and Super Sex will be the lovely and lovable result. Is there anything else to want?

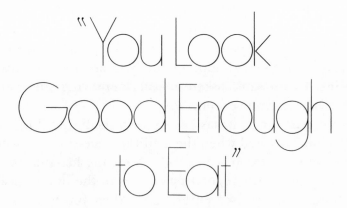

"You Look Good Enough to Eat"

Psychiatrists say that persons who utter those words mean them—exactly. It all goes back to oral gratification and other things psychological. As for me, I say that if you have an oral-gratification hangup, just think to what Super-Sexual purpose it can be used.

For starters, substitute a person for food, and you can construe that any way you like. One thing sure. Oral hangups—meaning too much drink, too much smoke, too much food—are usually merely substitutes for too little sex. Works just as well the other way around, happily. As for me—just pass me the substitute. OK?

When Dr. Abraham Friedman (in his book *How Sex Can Keep You Slim*) said, "Reach for your mate instead of your plate," he carved out a wonderful motto for me. I don't happen to have an oral-gratification hangup, but I'd always rather reach for my mate, and I *do* find I'm more likely to reach when I'm hungry for something. Better love than food. You can use that hangup to keep a lean-and-hungry look while you're enjoying the pleasures of Super Sex.

Not only that—sex itself uses up calories (hooray!), and Dr. Friedman tells us you can work out a mathematical formula for how much sex uses how many calories. I make it out to be 200 per screw, though I hear it's a bit more for whoever's on top. Then there are all those calories saved by your being too busy to get to the refrigerator. They add up. And they slim you down into the lithe Super-Sexual creature I want you to be. Not skinny. Lithe, and lean. That's what you want to be, but not, as I've said before, hungry to the point of extinction. You want to have a keen sexual appetite finely honed to enjoy the ultimate in Super Sex. By the same token, if you're enjoying Super Sex, you're going to be lean—as you've seen.

And, believe it or not, it has been shown medically (forgive me, but I'm always a bit surprised when the medical profession as a whole comes up with answers on sex; it seems to be *their* big hangup, too) that sex can *suppress* the appetite-regulating centers of the brain, meaning that if you're hungry for sex—or enjoying it—then you won't be thinking of food.

Dr. Eugene Scheimann (back again) tells us that oral gratifications are the way sexually frustrated people sublimate their normal sexual desires—in too much food, too much drink, too much smoke. (Some substitutes!) And he says substitutes are necessary only when sex and love are missing. Meaning, of course, they shouldn't be. Not for your health, not for your happiness, and not for your looks. At last all the doctors are saying, "Go ahead!" How terrific! One fun that isn't forbidden pleasure.

Shape Up—
Exercises to Reshape
Those Specific Spots

Obviously, what we are giving you is a book that will have you in such perfect shape that your sex life won't be the only thing that will be super. Your body will be too. However, for those who have small specific problems—such as upper arms that aren't firm enough, or thighs that don't always go down when weight does—we have exercises for them too.

Never forget, however, that every single exercise in this book works on almost every single muscle in your body, even though muscles needed for good sex are what we have in mind. In short, it's awfully hard to firm up your sexual body without making yourself shapely into the bargain. Therefore, you have gotten two benefits for the price of one exercise—done properly—Super Sex and super shape.

For those who want to know some specifics, here they are, but *never* eliminate something simply because you can't see the results immediately. You'll soon see them in your mirror. If you're not too busy with Super Sex to look.

For the neck, thighs and abdomen (some combination, what?): Stand erect with fingers clasped behind your neck. Pull your elbows back and raise one knee up, toes pointed, simply because it looks better and you may as well develop style while you're shaping. (A pointed toe also

works on the right muscles in the calf; so do it and make it look as good as you can!)

Hold this position for a few seconds—See if you can start with five. If you can hold the position for thirty seconds, then great.

Then repeat with the other knee.

Always remember to inhale when the elbows are pulled back and exhale when you come back to a standing position.

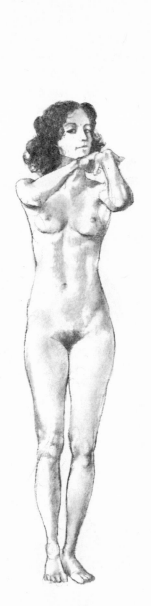
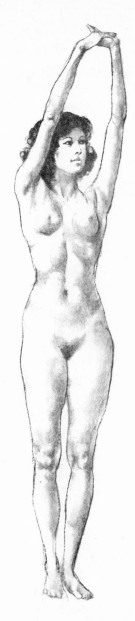

This one's important, for it's to firm the pushing muscles of the arm, which are the ones that tend to get flabby and look ugly—something we will not allow to happen. (For men, it just makes you stronger.)

Standing, bend the left arm and place the right hand on top of the left, just above your left shoulder.

Push the left arm above the head, resisting with the other, and return to original position—up and down, up and down.

Do this several times, and then repeat with the left hand on top. Make sure that you resist the pressure of your own pushing hand. That's what makes firm muscles. That's what makes pretty.

Aha! Now we've come to the bosom—and, for you guys out there, those manly muscles that you can ripple to every woman's content. These are for the chest, the pectorals (which keep the breasts ever erect, since the breast itself *is not muscle*), and for the entire firmness of the shoulder area—smooth, sleek, strong, and lovely.

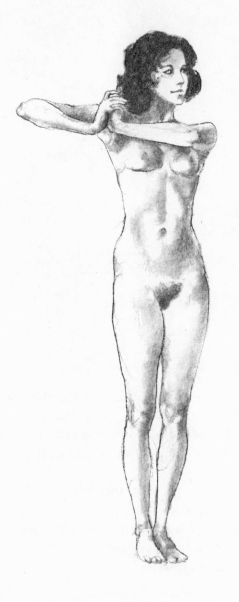 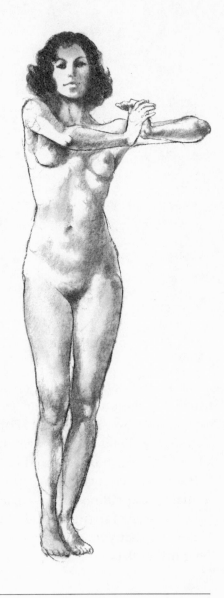

Standing or sitting, place one hand against the other at chest level. Slowly push from one side to the other, resisting with the hand being pushed. It is only from your own resistance that you get the strong muscles you need. Then try doing the same thing by moving the arms up and down, using the exact same resistance pressure. You're bound to feel it. You're also bound to see the results.

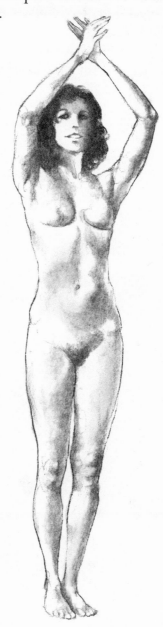

Here's one that reduces the waistline to gorgeous proportions, while it also works on the chest muscles, the stomach muscles and the thigh muscles. It would be hard to get much more mileage out of any single exercise. Nicholas somehow manages to work in a lot of muscles.

In a sitting position with your fingers clasped behind your head, bend one knee and, twisting your torso, try to reach your knee with the opposite elbow.

Exhale when your leg is bent and you are twisting. Then switch to the other leg. Inhale when you return to "start."

To Diet or Not...

How can you shape up without dieting? Well, let's talk about that. I have before me an advertisement for one of those reducing spas. The title reads: "Guys don't make passes at girls with fat ————." It's true—this is exactly the title. To which I say, "Like hell they don't."

You see, having made my reputation as a diet maven, I have now come to the realization that lean is wonderful, because it's healthy, because it makes you supple, because it makes you feel good, lighter, more energetic (and energy you'll need), and lean usually means one is hungry for sex. BUT—and this is a bigger "but"—lean is *not* skinny and skinny is not sexy and, since I tend to have a big one, I can swear that men *prefer* girls with ample asses and almost invariably make passes there!

Now all of you who have lost poundage along with me will doubtless close ranks in rancor, but I myself have deliberately put on ten pounds. For one thing, I caught a bad case of the flu, and I happen to be of the opinion that you shouldn't starve the flu unless you want to starve yourself right to death, since this decade's germs seem uncommonly vicious. I ate deliberately—and "ate deliberately" is the right term, since I still am reverent about *what* wholesome things I put inside of me, knowing full well they will soon show up on the outside of me.

On the other hand, I have found, throughout my life, that whenever I considered myself just a wee bit over the weight line, then the men came in hot pursuit. It has taken me this long to realize that men never make passes at girls with *flat* asses. A gentleman friend of mine explained it rather succinctly, saying, "Women see themselves *in* clothes, men see them *without* clothes." Therein lies the difference between the sexes. From now on, I want you to do what I did. Look at yourself with a cool eye in the mirror with *no* clothes. If there are sharp ribs showing, and flattened-from-dieting bosoms hanging and nothing on your bottom to pinch, then for God's sake, *put on some weight!*

For those out there who are genuinely overweight, I have no pity. Keep dieting! (Chances are you have men galore, but with a certain amount of sleekness to your body, you'll have a lot more agility for Super Sex.)

The simple fact of the shape of Super Sex is that it is indeed shapely. Keep its curves in mind.

Now I am going to try to give you a new look at dieting, and, hopefully, a new look for your body—your sexy, lush body. Gentlemen, don't get lost now! If there's one thing guaranteed to turn a woman off, it's the sight of a sickly-looking weakling of a man. I have a friend (and I hope he doesn't read this) who recently lost a total of *fifty* pounds. He could have used some loss, but—whereas before he was a not-so-tall and much-too-heavy sexpot of a man—he now is a tiny little thing who looks as if *I* could knock him over with a feather. I'm not the only one of his ex-fans who feels he lost his sexuality when he lost the fifty pounds. The other day we had lunch, and I quizzed him as I watched him do his starvation number. "Is your sex life as good as before?" And what do you think he confessed? That his virility was far below what it had been before thin. All of which should go to show you men that by overdieting you not only lose the weight but the strength you need for continued (yes, continued and continual and continuous) Super Sex and a lot of your sexuality to boot. You see, nothing turns a woman (most women) on more than a powerful-looking man. Nothing can turn her off faster than a runt. Take your choice as to which you'd rather be. I personally always go for the power, even if it comes with a touch of a paunch. I *do* want a man with the strength to sweep me off my feet whenever he chooses, without staggering in the process.

Therefore, I am going to ask you all, male and female alike, to do this:

Get a big full-length mirror (if you don't have one, *get* it) and check yourself *without your clothes*. Be as impersonal as you can, remembering that this is the Super-Sexual you your partner is going to see reflected in his/her eyes. We want you lean, all right. Sleek would be a better word. But think of the seal, that traditionally sleek creature. Is it skinny? Hell, no. Sleek, yes. Scrawny? Forget it. It makes an ugly reflection in your mirror and in your lover's eyes. Scrawny is decidedly and sexually out!

And so I am going to give you a new diet to follow; one that will keep you sleek as a seal and just as sexy.

First, figure out your ideal weight—the weight at which you think you look the very best. Add ten pounds and aim for that instead. You'll thank me later, when you have to bar your door against the pursuit of the opposite sex.

Fifteen hundred calories a day for women, 2,500 for men, should keep everybody in the right shape. Naturally, this is going to vary from person to person, depending on the individual metabolism. And individual it is, to the distress of everyone trying to diet. What's good for the goose isn't necessarily good for the gander in dieting.

Still, this should be the basic count to follow until you see whether you are achieving and/or maintaining your ideal weight.

Since I wrote *The Natural Way to Super Beauty*, I have been bombarded with requests for my own menus—what I eat each day. Well, what *I* eat each day might not at all agree with your own taste in food. And I must assure you that these days I do not eat to diet, and therefore am able to eat practically anything and everything I want. Sometimes I'm on a pasta kick, sometimes Indian food, sometimes Japanese cooking and often bacon and eggs—my favorite meal when I'm overtired, which is often, considering my hectic life. No, I am not concerned about cholesterol. I have never subscribed to the cholesterol-scare theory, and a great many medical men are beginning to think my way. In any case, the lecithin I take so religiously will deal effectively with the cholesterol-producing foods I may take in. Don't think I haven't checked with my doctor. My cholesterol is practically subzero, in spite of the bacon-and-egg penchant.

But there is one thing I never fail to include in my daily meal, and

I know that a great many of you are going to ask me whether or not I still abide by my own discovery—namely, the dietary supplements of kelp, lecithin, cider vinegar, and vitamin B-6—the supplements that turned the whole world's thinking to thin, and made an awful lot of money for companies that produced "magic" capsules for those too lazy to down the real things. No wonder millions of people ask me, "Why did I stop losing weight when I started taking those pills?" My answer: "Because I don't believe there's anything in them." This is it, and if any manufacturer chooses to prove to me that they contain precisely my formula, then let him step forward. Until that time, I must insist you be brave, swallow the vinegar, take the kelp and B-6, and eat your lecithin—all *daily*. That's the only way this formula works, and it works to keep you healthy (and sexy), whether you're dieting or not.

I attribute my sudden (after all of these years of dieting) ability to eat whatever my heart and stomach desire *without gaining weight* to my four little friends: cider vinegar, B-6, kelp and lecithin. They will, forever, remain a part of my daily bread.

Speaking of bread, there are some false ideas that I believe ought to be cleared up here and now. First of all, bread is not only not fattening (eaten normally, of course, and not a loaf at a sitting) but essential to your health, as good bread—and I stress the word "good," meaning made from unbleached flour as opposed to that white glue that often passes for bread—contains the B vitamins so necessary to your health, to your hair's health, to the health of your nails and, really, to all of your beautiful self.

Pasta is another supposedly fat food that is much maligned. I'm not speaking about slimy overcooked spaghetti, but rather wonderfully cooked, al dente, preferably homemade pasta. Check the calories. You'll find they're nowhere near as high as those of meat—any meat, but most particularly beef.

Beef, of course, is my pet peeve. The healthful properties of beef are mythical. Yes, it's protein, but yes, it's fattening, and its protein is far from the most or the best you can get. The greatest mistake most dieters make is in believing that a steak and salad is diet food. A steak has one hundred (yes, 100) calories to the forkful, and a small shell steak can contain a day's worth of calories, so think it over before you think steak. Its value just may not be worth the weight.

Enough, however, of my pet peeves and pet loves. I am going to tell you once and for all (and once again, so no one will ask me again) what *I* eat. Do with it what you will.

For breakfast I indulge in my favorite food, bacon. Three slices. (Yes, I know all about nitrites, and I think they're harmful, but there's so much stuff in all our food that I've simply given up trying to make sure it's pure and decided to indulge myself in *some* food-vice now and again. Crisp bacon is my vice and delight.) Then, for breakfast dessert, I eat my never-missed three tablespoons of raw wheat germ topped off by the requisite tablespoon of lecithin granules (that's important since it's the most potent form of lecithin) all covered with half and half. When I'm really pampering myself, I go with heavy cream. Sound like diet fare to you? For me, it's heaven. You see, I have rare tastes, which is why I have hesitated to tell you what they are. They probably won't be yours, but, on the other hand, the wheat germ and lecithin combination should be a requisite for you all because it contains that Super-Sexy vitamin E, and the lecithin makes sure the fat keeps moving and never lands in your arteries as fat. Besides, lecithin also contains two terrific hair vitamins—inositol and choline—both members of the B-complex and both usually missing from any all-purpose B-vitamin capsule. Wheat germ also grows you sexy hair, so you have nothing to lose and lots to gain by making it a staple on your breakfast menu.

When I am home in Alabama—meaning someone else is doing the cooking—my somewhat Spartan breakfast tastes change dramatically to grits with butter, homemade biscuits, country ham—you name it. If it's good Southern fare, I eat it, and I haven't an extra pound to show for my visits South.

As for luncheon—well, that depends. It depends mostly on where I happen to be at the time. Once again, Southerners eat a full meal at lunch as well as at dinner. Don't ask *me* why they aren't all chubby. Could be because their choice of food is so wise—not through any fault of their own. It simply happens to be traditional to lunch on fried chicken, or fresh crab meat or shrimp, plus at least three different *fresh* vegetables. In spite of the fact that Alabama is the cattle land of the South, having surpassed Texas (we think) for the best beef in the country, Southerners where I come from still go for that old fried chicken, to the unsuspecting betterment of their health—and shapes. For chicken, even fried, has far fewer calories than steak. And, to boot, all Southerners are given iced tea as a matter of habit by every knowledgeable restaurateur in lieu of wine. Could be because good wine is hard to come by there. Could be because wine makes you hotter. But even when the thermometer's near zero, iced tea is the requisite drink. It's as refreshing as wine and, unsugared, has something like 1 calorie per glass. Try it and like it. It will preserve your looks—from your shape to your skin. If you hate tea, iced coffee will do.

New York is another breed of city. In New York, once again, it depends on where I'm lunching. If it's in my own home, then the less the better. I loathe cooking, and there's simply no way out of that admission. And so, I'll opt for a grilled-cheese sandwich. Yes, sandwich, liberally laced with mayonnaise and covered with polyunsaturated margarine (not butter)—the skinnier (read "slimmer") to make you, my dears. Generally, I have a fresh fruit—even stewed fruit (always without sugar)—to wind up the meal.

Dinner is the same all over. Meat or fish, but *no* beef. There is chicken or lamb, or fish, or oysters (yeah, oysters) or cheese soufflé (full of protein), or even pasta. Along with it? Garden (or what passes for "garden" in New York) fresh vegetables, not overcooked. Sometimes one, sometimes two. Always ending with fruit.

I'll tell you now that I have a lifetime hatred for citrus fruits, can't understand for the life of me how anyone can stomach orange juice on an empty gut in the A.M., and I don't see any signs of scurvy for me. Could be because I adore tomatoes, which are full of vitamin C. In any case, I seem to get plenty, because too much additional C—except when I ward off a cold—usually gives me a rash. No, it isn't my imagination, and so I can only assume I have all the C I need from natural sources and thus limit my own intake of vitamin C supplements to 500 milligrams per day. But, then, I don't smoke, and smoking devours vitamin C almost faster than you can down it. Soon, I hope, medicine will know more about exactly which vitamins each individual requires. Until then, it's strictly trial and error.

Now that you know a typical food-day in the life of Mary Ann Crenshaw and promise not to ask me for my menus (I never know them until that moment of truth when I must face the stove), I will tell you flat out: *Don't do as I do, do as I say.* I feel sure that most of you don't have the peculiar innards I seem to have, and therefore I will lay out some typical menus to keep you healthy as well as well-shaped. Meaning shapely. Here we go with a menu for a healthy, sexy human:

BREAKFAST

Cereal. *Not*, please, those empty, worthless sugared things always named something cute like "Krunchie Krispies," but, instead, something that will add to your vitamin intake, like oatmeal, cream of wheat, shredded wheat, and, best of all, wheat germ, topped off, of course, with lecithin granules and covered with cream. Delicious, slenderizing and good. Good for you, too.

Poached egg on toast (made with "good" bread) with safflower oil margarine, the best of the polyunsaturates and loaded with sexy vitamin E.

Bacon, ham—any meat but beef. (Even kippers if you stomach them well!)

Coffee, tea, milk.

LUNCHEON

Here's where I prefer to take it light. It's tough to concentrate on work when you're loaded down with a heavy intake of food. So try: Broiled fish or plain boiled fish. Or shrimp with butter and garlic. You may even have the rice (45 calories per cup—less than a piece of bread). Mixed green salad with oil and vinegar. Roquefort dressing if you prefer. If there's homemade bread present, by all means have some. For *dessert, nothing* more "sweety pie" than fresh fruit. Cheese. Coffee. *No sugar!*

I happen to disapprove of all the bad things refined sugar has done to our lives. It's one of the worst enemies of good health and has helped to ruin the lives of more people in this world than you can imagine. For example, did you realize that diabetes is now the number-three killer in the United States? And did you realize that too much sugar is one of the prime factors in diabetes? *Leave off sugar!* If sweeten you must, use one of the sugar substitutes—whichever one the FDA has declared safe for this year's use, since they seem to vacillate each year. *Never make the mistake of believing that honey isn't sugar too.* It isn't refined, which is all to the good, but it *is* sugar, and I'd forget it. In fact, I do.

DINNER

For dinner, go to it. Just remember that you must sleep afterward, and that sleep after a heavy meal is going to make the meal stick with, and to, your body. If you eat earlier (in the South we make it 6:30, which at first I found intolerable, later sensible), you have more time for the meal to disappear before bed. And, remember the old adage—you can't (or shouldn't) make love on a full stomach. Not good love, anyway, so either eat earlier or eat less. For Super Sex's sake.

Fried or broiled chicken. (You see? Why not?)

Southern-style green beans (cooked with bacon). Why not?

Rice and gravy (yes, it's OK).

Brussels sprouts (don't overdo it—high calories here).

Homemade rolls or bread (here you don't overdo either).

Coffee, tea, but preferably no milk again.

For dessert, either whip up some nonsugared dessert, or have cheese and fruit with your coffee.

This is a Southern menu all right. In Yankee land, I eat:

Lamb chops, broiled

Brussels sprouts (again, limited)

Green beans almondine

Stewed fruit

Coffee

Or I eat out, where I can go the range from pasta to Japanese, to French, sauces and all, as long as I stay away from the known "baddies," beef and sugar.

Vegetables should always be *under*cooked rather than overcooked. Vitamins have a way of disappearing into the air under the heat of cooking, so to keep them in, eat your vegetables *al dente*. Better still, eat them raw.

Does that answer any questions about what *I* eat? I may just have chosen some of your pet hate foods that are my favorites, so how on earth can I make up a palatable menu for you?

There are, however, a few simple guidelines to remember on what isn't good for you, and what is and what isn't fattening.

I will never understand how all the myths have been propagated about fattening foods, but I will try to explode some of them here.

Rice. Look at the Orientals who live on it three times per day. The ones who are obese are usually the ones who have taken to Western ways and Western menus. Rice alone is far from fattening, having fewer calories than bread. Which brings us to . . .

Bread. Seventy-five calories per slice. With beef at 100 calories per forkful, which would you choose? Once again, I refer to good, wholesome, preferably homemade-from-whole-flour bread—not the useless gooey sort. Whether it's white or whole wheat makes a difference in taste only. If the flour is right, bread is indeed the staff of life. Eat some every day.

Potatoes. Guess what? A baked potato, skin and all equals 141 calories. Big deal. And nothing is better for you than all those vitamins that stick to the skin of a potato. Give up something less nutritious. I disapprove of French fries for the saturated fats they're generally fried in, but the potato is a much-maligned vegetable. Try to reconsider its food value.

Fats. Fats are not fattening. Fats are essential. Fats are not unhealthy. Fats are important to health. Polyunsaturated fats—those that are liquid at room temperature—are the healthiest sort with safflower oil and safflower margarine heading my list of must-eats. I find that the more safflower margarine I eat, the slimmer I become, regardless of my menus. Besides that, unsaturated fats are high in the sex-vitamin E, and so their need, when you're thinking Super Sex, should be obvious. And if you want to look your loveliest/handsomest, with shining, thick hair and glowing, clear skin, then *fats are a must-eat!* Without them, you simply dry up.

Pasta. Every soul alive with weight loss in mind cringes at that word. Why, I don't know. Pasta should be homemade, and in good Italian restaurants it is. Homemade with good flour (there we go again) and occasionally with such exotics as artichoke and spinach flour—the better to vitamin you with. Pasta has fewer calories than meat. Pasta has vitamin B. Pasta is good for you. Within normal serving limits, just like everything else. Gluttony will not keep you slender.

Sugar. Sugar is simply a no-no. Forever and ever. Refined sugar will help shorten your life, if that's what you really want. I don't, and so I have renounced sugar for the rest of what I hope will be my long, sex-filled days.

Honey. Honey has a reputation for being a health food. But honey is still sugar, and as such, can do the same sort of harm. It may take a bit longer, since honey is decidedly better than refined sweets, but honey is sweet and honey can send your body into a sugar-drunk tailspin, turning you into diabetic or hypoglycemic (which isn't the opposite of diabetes, just a peculiar sort of forerunner of that killer disease). *Do not think of honey as health food.* It isn't.

Meat. Why is it that every man alive thinks that a huge steak is going to make him more manly? In truth it may have exactly the opposite effect. With Americans' taste for the easy life, beef-cattle people have learned that we're too lazy even to chew, and so have made life easier by injecting beef with diethylstylbestrol, a *female* hormone that makes cattle collapse on the hoof if it gets to them before the axe falls. Adelle Davis accused this hormone of causing the extraordinary upswing of female characteristics in American males today.

A red-blooded American male? Well, the meat may be American red-blooded, but you won't be so all-fired male, so think about that every time you order a big, manly steak. Consider the lowly hamburger as equally dangerous meat.

The lighter meats, such as lamb, and even pork, are going to make you feel neat-on-your-feet, in your bed and wherever you need to do any fancy footwork. Chicken, fish, cheese, all have wonderful protein (that's what you think you need steak for) and are much better for you. The number of people who have told me they voluntarily gave up beef in the past year is enlightening. And every one of them claims to feel better for so doing. So do it.

Now. Have I filled you full of menus of good things to eat? I hope so, and I hope I have impressed upon you that good eating makes for good looking, good feeling, and therefore good sex. There is no way on earth to separate healthy from sexy. I wouldn't want to try.

Just try to remember the basics given here and base your own menus on your own tastes, eliminating the no-nos and going for the yes-indeedies. They're here for your own good.

The Panic Button
(For Emergency Use
Only!)

I know that somewhere out there, there's someone who's going to say that he or she needs a crash diet. Horrors! I can't have that, but I *am* sympathetic with the terrible realization one has upon seeing that pounds have gone on where pounds shouldn't be, and it's bikini time, or party time, or even super-seduction time. For moments like these, and only if one has absolutely come to the conclusion that the pounds are bulges and not just lush flesh, then —and only then—will I condone a diet that will help you get everything back in a flash. Two diets, in fact, for two kinds of dieters. But always and always to be taken with my four little friends: cider vinegar, kelp, lecithin, vitamin B-6 which, as you will see, are to be taken whether you're dieting or not.

The two diets for which I have complete respect are simple—so simple, in fact, that crash-dieters may decide to go off on their own and end up crashing for sure. Once again, no sympathy here. Your health is what I aim to care for, and if you want to be stupid about it, then leave me here and now.

I believe in the value of the famous low-carbohydrate diet. It's been called everything in the world, from drinking man's diet, to high-fat diet (which it isn't), to everybody's diet, when in fact it has been around since 1863 and is the standard diet for diabetics (and one they'd better stick to or die). It is, I believe, the fastest way to weigh in at your ideal point, *as long as* you stop dieting there. You see, this diet has some strange things about it. It can backfire and play tricks on your innards that will do them no good.

To my mind, six weeks is the maximum anyone should stay on this particular diet. After that, no matter how good you are at sticking to it, it may have peculiar side effects and even go so far as to make you *fat*. Therefore, this is a healthy diet as long as it is followed with care (and with a doctor's care). It is, as well, the very best diet for those with the most weight to lose. For some reason, the more that needs to go, the faster it goes on this diet. It also has the supreme advantage of taking the heft off the places you've got it and not off the places you need it—muscles for men, bosoms for women, for examples. Nor does it give that diet-scrawny look to the face and neck, the look that I'm campaigning against for both men and women, for nothing's less attractive than a skinny neck, whether it's got a loose collar and tie surrounding it, or a low-to-no-bosom dress.

The diet is simplicity itself. All that's required is a working knowledge of what the carbohydrate count of any given food is.

Dr. Robert C. Atkins was my physician when I learned by practice about this particular way of dieting. Thank goodness he was there, for with my peculiar medical make-up, naturally, I had some problems. You just might have some unsuspected ones too, and so I am going to say, as I always do whenever the subject of diet comes up, never, *never* undertake *any* diet without the tender loving care of your physician to back you up. This is a dieter's must. Even for short periods. Your health is nothing to play do-it-yourself with.

The high-protein, low-carbohydrate diet—or the other way round, if it pleases you—is the sort I believe my fifty-pound loser (and sex weakling) should have gone on. It would have allayed any of the weakness he ascribes to his 1,000 calories per day—something he doomed himself to hold to, with its ensuing problem of loss of sexual appetite. What good does it do to be fifty pounds lighter if, out of sheer weakness, you can't make it sexually? That isn't what I'd ever recommend for anyone—even the supposedly weaker sex (meaning us dames).

Here's how the low carbohydrate diet goes:

The no-go foods on this diet are starches and sweets. Simple? You bet. The only complication is in knowing what is starchy and what is sweet. For example, I'll bet you didn't know that orange juice is supremely high in carbohydrates, as are tomato paste, onions and a few other innocuous-appearing foods.

That is why you must have at hand, at all times, a reliable carbohydrate counter, to be checked at each mouthful.

Liquor is allowed (thus the "drinking man's diet" label), but you may be surprised to find that wine has many more carbohydrates than hard liquor, with champagne right at the top of the no-no list. If you find you're not losing weight, however, *all* alcohol must go, since alcohol turns to carbohydrates within the body, meaning "zero" on the chart may become "carbohydrate" in you.

The Atkins version of this diet requires that you begin with a week of *no* carbohydrates. In my opinion, you can start with "low." Eat nothing that contains more than 10 carbohydrates (this does not mean 10 per day, it means 10 per food item), and you're home free. If that isn't an easy diet to remember, then I don't know one.

Pretty soon, your body, needing its daily bread, will begin to use up not the fat you need but the extraneous fat you are out to get rid of as quickly as possible. The scale should begin to dip from the first day until the last, when you've reached your ideal weight. But don't forget my lecture. Ideal is *not* skin-and-bones, and no bikini ever looked good on a body shaped like a bean pole. I am speaking to women now, because I am one. We seem to have peculiar ideas about how we appeal to men. My man always accused me of wanting a body like a boy's. I never really believed him until one day we were taxiing down the street when I saw, from the rear, a gorgeous blonde creature with just the figure I'd always longed to have. Can you imagine my chagrin when we passed the figure? I turned to see what beautiful face topped off that fantastic body, only to find it was a man! From that day forward, I've never lusted after a boy's body except in the normal way . . . lusted after a boy, period.

So here's how you go about reshaping yourself (in a hurry, in an emergency) the low-carbohydrate way:

EMERGENCY DIET #1

1. You are allowed to have all the meat you want—please keep in mind what I said about beef. Beef, in fact, is the first thing you give up when the weight stops going down.

2. You may indulge yourself in any amount of bacon, eggs and other good breakfast things.

3. You may *not* have orange juice (sugar) or any fruit that goes above that 10-carbohydrate mark. If you can stay below that with wonderful ripe strawberries, or melon, or any other relatively low-sugar fruit, go right ahead.

4. You may *not* have any sweets whatsoever, or any foods that are processed in syrup or sweetened in any way. *Check the labels on prepared foods for this*. If there is sugar, back away!

5. *You may not have milk* (or yogurt). You may have all the cream your heart desires.

6. You may have butter, margarine or other fats within reason. *I* say within reason because, while they have zero carbohydrates, too much fat can have bad reactions on certain parts of your digestive tract (it got me in the pancreas, of all things) and so be careful, careful and careful with overdoing the fats. Have them, by all means. Just don't get greedy.

7. You may *not* have any organ meats, such as liver (a storehouse for sugar), sweetbreads and the like, or any meat with fillers such as bologna.

8. You may have salad until you sprout rabbit ears.

9. You may have a half cup of vegetables per day or the 10-carbohydrate equivalent thereof. Here's where you really need that carbohydrate chart, since some vegetables, like peas and beans, are starchy and therefore full of carbohydrates, while others, such as string beans, are low. Check before you eat.

10. You may *not* have bread during this diet period.

These are the basics, but if you remember to forget all starches, all sweets (including anything that tastes sweet), then you're already on the low-carbohydrate diet and well on your weigh to lower weight.

Here's a fast recap on no-no foods for this diet:
No sugar
No soft drinks
No starch
No organ meats (lots of stored sugar)
No luncheon meats with cereal fillers (bologna, etc.)

No beans except string beans
No potatoes
No fruit (except below-10-carbohydrate fruits)
No bread
No milk (high in carbohydrates)

Watch out for: Tomatoes (sweet), onions (ditto), catsup (sugar-loaded), sweet pickles, chewing gum, sweetened medicines, such as cough syrup, and anything that has the slightest sweet taste to you, including some Oriental sauces. When in doubt, question. If a waiter rebels, tell him you're diabetic and will die at the table. That generally generates the truth!

Never take in more than a half cup of vegetables per day, and if you eat your low-carbo fruit (the only fruit allowed) you have had your half cup.

No more than one glass of wine per day, remember? Alcohol doesn't have carbohydrates, but it can make them inside of you, so watch it with booze. Besides that, with nothing to sop up the liquor, your gut will suffer.

If you keep everything at the 10-carbohydrate count, you should be home free and thin. If not, cut the count down.

Then there's the other diet (you see, I recognize only two as safe, and I need you safe and sexy), the low-calorie regime. That should be a cinch for anyone, but apparently plenty of people, who obviously can't count, don't understand. There's a foolproof way to check your calories, but it, too, involves checking a calorie counter. And then learning to write! I have just been reading an article in a national magazine that tells how to make sure about dieting. It said that keeping a notebook is a must if you want to know where your possible cheating is. Could just be mistakes. In any case, when it comes to calorie counting you can't count to 10 and stop. You must write down everything that goes into your body via your mouth and next to it the number of calories you have just taken in. At the end of each meal, total the number. At the end of each day, do a total for the day.

For women who want to take it off fast, 1,000 calories is the number. For men, I'd make it 1,500 (as long as you're not weak, in which case 1,750 should do nicely).

EMERGENCY DIET #2

Remember the following: Beef is plenty fattening. Booze is worse. Give it up for your emergency period. Sweets are a definite no. As for sweetened coffee, use a sugar substitute.

As for what you *can* eat, the answer is everything. My reason for the definite "no" on sweets is because they're bad for you and I don't want you giving up your health and your 1,000 calories per day to a single piece of cake. The cake you'll get at the end of your emergency diet will be rewarding enough.

The main thing is that, on a low-calorie diet, there are no restrictions as long as you keep that notebook, and do not cheat (it's yourself you'll be cheating). Make sure you get your protein, and lots of it, because you'll be needing the strength. Remember, fish, cheese, fowl and all sorts of good things contain protein. Fattening beef is not the end-all to protein intake.

You may choose any favorite vegetable, as long as you make sure to add accurately and carefully in your diet notebook. If you choose to dine on vegetables alone, why not?

Fruits of any sort can be included on this diet, once again, making sure your calorie count is accurate.

By the end of six weeks you should see yourself as you wish to see yourself, keeping in mind always to see yourself *nude* in your mirror. You'll see the reflection in your partner's eyes.

A Visit with
My Old Friends

Cider vinegar. Kelp. Lecithin. Vitamin B-6. I just want to get one thing straight before we go on. You probably all know me as the dame who came up with the famous cider vinegar, B-6, kelp and lecithin diet. If anyone came up with that combo before me, let him or her speak up now or ever after get out of my diet. Because more people have made more money using my name falsely (thank heaven I have lawyers) and using you falsely by insinuating that they made capsules containing the proper dosages of these four magic dietary supplements, i.e., the "four little friends" I found and reported on—accurately—in my book *The Natural Way to Super Beauty*. Until now I have had no place to speak up publicly and scream, as I wish to do, about the practically fraudulent advertising that accompanies these close-to-fraudulent pills. I will simply state as clearly as I can that any pills claiming to contain the four little friends probably contain them all right, but *they do not contain the dosage I recommend in my book*. Want to know how I can be so sure? Because I know the Food and Drug Administration won't permit them to, just as they now won't permit you to take the vitamins that I, and many others far more medically knowledgeable than myself (like Linus Pauling and his ilk) believe you should have. This does *not* mean, however, that there is any danger in the "four little friends." Would I do that to you? Oh no.

I checked out the experts on endocrinology—that science of human metabolic tricks—to find that my dosage was so low it had never even been tested but that dosages up to two hundred times as large had been found safe! Should that not put everyone's heart at rest? Kelp was the question considered here. Kelp passed the test. But what *I* know and you didn't, until now, was that those wily pill-makers *could not*, by law, put into their capsule covers more than one third the amount of kelp I myself take! As for cider vinegar in a capsule . . . perhaps modern technology can do it, but why? It simply says a lot for the laziness of the American woman, who's always looking for the easy way, and often losing her looks to the search. Sorry, ladies. I have no patience. (My impatience includes lazy men.) To those who stop losing weight when they start taking those capsules I sharply say, "It serves you right." And it does. Any easy way is usually not the best way. In the case of pills like these it is no way at all.

And so I've said it for any knock-offs of my four little friends, which are, I might add, still serving me perfectly well in keeping off any unwanted flesh. I still never eat a meal, nor discuss nutrition or health or beauty or sex with *anybody* without that somebody asking me (generally skeptically) whether or not I really stick with my four little friends—the famous four that helped America reach its ideal weight.

The answer is *yes*! Whether I am trying to put on weight (which is more the case since the four friends came into my previously fat-fighting life) or not, I end each and every meal with my cider vinegar brew, my four or five kelp tablets, and my vitamin B-6 in the 50-milligram unit form. Lecithin is for breakfast.

Obviously, if I am dining out in some posh restaurant, I don't pull all of this out of my handbag in public. But I do rush for it the moment I get home. On the other hand, if, for some reason, you can't get to your four friends at lunchtime, be assured that twice a day is far better than no times a day, and make it your business to get the brew downed at least that often.

If there is ever any way to get my exact formula into a capsule, I can promise you that my name will be the one endorsing it. The number of people who have tried to buy that good name for their worthless (my own opinion) products is appalling. Never will I let my readers down when it's a matter of integrity versus payoff-payroll. And so I have turned down offer after offer. And yet manufacturers of these so-called miracle pills go right on selling them by the billions to readers who want the results without the effort. For me, drinking a glass of water and swallowing a few pills is very little effort compared to the immediately obvious results.

If you want a placebo, take the capsules. If you want to keep your weight in line, take the original four friends.

I think, however, you deserve a stronger (perhaps) repetition of the value of the fabulous four. Maybe then you'll understand them and stick by them, for they can be your four most valuable friends for the rest of your life.

Cider vinegar. There are some who say they can't stand the taste. I don't believe for a moment that they are taking the right sort of vinegar or diluting it as they should. Health-food-store natural apple cider vinegar is the sort you want. One *teaspoonful* to a tumbler of water. When it's diluted to that extent, all you can taste is something appley. What's so bad about that? If it's the thought of vinegar that gets to your stomach, then just don't think.

Vinegar can be considered a *digestif,* since it helps return the stomach to its normal (yes, normal) state of acidity, the only state in which it can digest, and thus utilize, food.

Therefore, consider it lemonade, an after-dinner drink, whatever. But *get it down!*

Kelp. Kelp is seaweed. My recommended dosage is four tablets of kelp with each glass of cider vinegar. I swallow them all together, meaning one big gulp. Now *that's* not so tough, is it? No more than taking an aspirin, and you probably down those as a matter of course, even though you should be as careful with aspirin as with any other drug. They're not for casual swallowing. Kelp, on the other hand, is only seaweed. The Japanese eat seaweed with almost every meal. The Irish do as well—some Irish eat dulse like candy—and check their skin if you want to see clear. (Not clearly, clear skin.) Kelp contains the iodine (.15 mg. per tablet) that gets your metabolism working properly, and whether yours is low or high, it matters not. Kelp works as a *normalizer*, setting the metabolism right, no matter which turn it may have taken.

Now, a metabolism in working order is essential to keeping weight under control, whether you want it higher or lower.

I was shocked, after the publication of *Super Beauty*, by the number of vicious and apparently unlearned attacks on poor little harmless kelp by those who should know better, and that includes nutritionists and even some medical men who certainly ought to get back to their books. It also includes some nutritionists who use their Ph.D.-acquired title "Dr." and therefore pass themselves off to unsuspecting readers as doctors of medicine. Frankly, I was so disturbed I went, as I said, to the highest experts of this land, just to be sure (*I* was, but I had to try to convince everyone else) that there was no harm in the amount of kelp I recommended.

Once again, this is what I found. There has never been any research done on amounts as *low* as what I recommend. On amounts *two hundred* times higher than my dosages there was still no appreciable ill effects, i.e., none worth noting. Naturally, someone out there may have an allergy problem, just as some people can't sleep on feather pillows and I can. But this doesn't stop the world from using feather pillows, or riding horses, or owning cars. In short, the world can't give up its ways for the allergic few, though I am hoping that at any sign of allergy you will quickly give up *any* substance that you believe may be the culprit. No matter how good it is, it obviously isn't good for *you*. Since I am not with each and every one of you, I expect you to exercise expert judgment in the behavior of your own body, and, for God's sake (and your body's), do not carry on with anything at all that appears to disagree with you. But, at the same time, don't claim it's dangerous to others.

As far as I am concerned, doctors and nutritionists who make such unproven claims are the kind of so-called experts I steer clear of. They're a lot more dangerous than kelp!

I hope that answers all questions about my concern for your safety. If these offhand types don't care, I do! Take your kelp, and remember that entire nations (like the Japanese) aren't dead because of their seaweed tastes. Pretty silly to worry, isn't it?

Now—and I want to make this clear once and for all—I take my cider-vinegar-and-kelp brew after every single meal, *three times per day*. These are the only two of the four friends that are to be taken thrice daily. Here's how you do the others:

B-6—the wonder vitamin that reduces your waistline without reducing all of you—is the one and only B vitamin I have ever dared to separate from its complex whole. Vitamin B-6 works its miracles when taken in 50-milligram doses per day. Have you got that? A *total* of 50 milligrams a day. I don't care whether you take your B-6 tablet once a day at 50 milligrams or twice at 25 milligrams each per day or in your B-complex capsule, if it happens to contain that much, which I doubt. *All I care about is that you receive a total of fifty milligrams of B-6 per day.* No more, no less.

Lecithin—oh lovely, lithely lecithin, purveyor of vitamin E, and all the good-hair B's—how I love you! Lecithin is the miracle that is made from soybeans; it's a pure fat (the granules are fat reduced to granular form) and it should go to prove how beautiful fats can make you.

Lecithin keeps the *un*wanted fat moving off your body, it acts as a healthy, natural diuretic, and it makes you lean, sexy and beautiful. As far as I am concerned, it's soybean's greatest contribution to a healthy, sexy American population.

I eat my lecithin granules—and I stress *granules* once more since they are the most potent form of lecithin—on top of my wheat germ (the wheat germ I'm eating every day anyway). Once again, do not be misled into swallowing lecithin capsules . . . you'd be swallowing all day to get enough. You can also dissolve the granules in your orange juice, if that's your morning drink, or even in water, which isn't half as tasty. The important thing is that you get it in this dosage: *1 tablespoon per day*. You will note *I did not say after every meal*, I said *per day*! Actually, you can go to 2 tablespoons if you so desire, bearing in mind that lecithin, as it is a fat, does have calories. If it's more weight you're after, go for more. But for most of us once per day is enough.

Just in case, on the second-book go-around, there are still any questions as to what *I* take, here it is again:

1 tablespoonful of lecithin *once a day*

1 50-milligram B-6 tablet *once a day*

4 to 5 kelp tablets *three times a day*, taken in cider-vinegar brew, which is . . . 1 *tea*spoon of apple cider vinegar in a tumbler of water *three* times a day

If there are any questions now, I will beat a hasty retreat.

One or Two "No's"

There are several things that must never be used, even in a panic-button emergency. They are dangerous. They can ruin your sex life. They can ruin your own life. They can *kill*!

Those things are diet pills, diuretics and starvation.

Let's begin with diet pills. If I could only tell you the number of idiots (no, I won't be kind here) I know who pop a diet pill when they don't even need to lose weight, but have simply decided they do and, obviously, have accommodating doctors to dole out prescriptions. Diet pills are dangerous. Diet pills are amphetamines. Amphetamines are, in street language, "speed." Speed kills. And how. First it kills your looks, makes your hair fall out, makes your teeth fall out, makes your flesh fall away, turns your brain to jelly, and, finally, kills you. Do you truly think any weight loss is worth all that? Do you *really* believe that a drug like speed is going to make you beautiful? When you're six feet under, will anyone care that the corpse is thin? You'll be thin all right . . . skin and bones are all that will remain. *Stay away from diet pills.* They aren't amusing.

Diuretics remain one of the most abused drugs extant. So many people who simply overeat get their kicks out of blaming it all on water. Water just happens to be essential to your well-being and, most particularly, to the beauty of hair, skin, and all of you. It's what keeps you from being dry and shriveled.

Diuretics do nothing more than rid your body of valuable water, and, in the process, rid it of valuable minerals, with potassium being the one that's most dangerous to lose. The loss of water from diuretics is temporary in any case and, since fat contains no water at all, has nothing whatsoever to do with the state of fat on your body. The most diuretics can do is make you unhealthy, and that isn't sexy. *Stay away from diuretics*—and stop kidding yourself.

Most crash diets are the bane of my existence—everything from grapefruit diets (grapefruit is good for you if taken with food) to virtual-starvation routines. These are bound to make you lose weight all right, since your body won't be getting what it needs to sustain anything, much less its healthy good looks. And, I might add, remember the saga of the fifty-pounds-lighter-but-starving-and-sexless man. Weakness is generally the result of any form of crash diet, since the necessary nutrients are never included. True fasting should, of course, only be undertaken in a hospital under the constant care of a physician, and even then there is some evidence that it does irreparable damage. Why shouldn't it? Your body needs fuel and you need your body and there'll be no Super Sex forthcoming from a weakened and wizened you. Therefore, for my sake, for your sake, for your partner's sake and in the name of Super Sex, *forgo crash diets*!

If diet you must, push only two (one at a time) of the panic buttons I've okayed as safe for you and your sex life. Deal?

Is It True
What They Say
About Oysters?

What you mean, I'll bet, is do aphrodisiacs really exist? Well, they do all right, and if you're as smart as I think you are, you'll steer clear of them. Aphrodisiacs ain't ambrosia. Real aphrodisiacs are simply bladder irritants, with the worst of them being even worse—poison. Spanish fly, for example, which is undoubtedly the most famous of the lot, is nothing more than cantharis, a highly poisonous substance made from the crushed wings of Spanish beetles. Sound tempting to you? Just don't try it on me, I beg of you! It is used both as a diuretic and an aphrodisiac, but the lethal dosage for man is about .03 grams. I will leave it to the beetles. (Or should I have said it's for the birds?)

Alcohol got its aphrodisiacal reputation because of the fact that it, too, is a bladder irritant to a certain extent. It will turn you on—for a while—but it's sure to let you down (and you men may take that literally) when overused.

In general, anything claiming to be an aphrodisiac is simply bad news unless you want to fool around with irritating your bladder beyond repair. I must hasten to add, however, that if you are ever invaded by some germ that causes bladder irritation (and they are common, such irritations) then don't feel surprised if you feel "turned on." It happened to me and I was frankly shocked at my feelings until my doctor explained the whole connection between bladder and sexual organs, proving how *closely* connected the two are and how important it is for you to keep doing those "inner" exercises. As for being turned on— forget aphrodisiacs and have a turned-on partner close at hand. It's a lot more fun.

If, however, you want to know whether foods like oysters have any aphrodisiacal effect—well, that's a tough question. Know why? It isn't the sort of thing most of the food agencies give answers on.

My feeling is that all food that is good for you is good for your sex life, and there are some that are downright turn-ons, though I truly can't make a sworn statement about oysters. They're full of protein power, and power helps, as we all know. Fish, as an entire family, as one of the better sources of protein, doesn't give you that too-heavy-to-do-it feeling and contains the iodine you need to keep your metabolism whirring away at keeping you lean enough to be lithe.

Certain foods are certified as containing nutrients that *I* know (yes, from experience) make you turned on sexually. Vitamin E for one. E the sexpot vitamin. E for energy (didn't I tell you that you can't separate health and vigor from sex?). I was reading an article about one of my health gurus, Carlton Fredericks, recently, wherein he maintains that vitamin E is *not* the sex vitamin "some self-styled experts" have hinted it is. I don't know what Dr. Fredericks meant, but I *do* know that he told *me* that he had to cut down on vitamin E for the same reason I told him I had. That is, the sexual excitement was interfering with our work . . . his somewhere else, mine here. I have never met Dr. Fredericks, although we have had some delightful telephone conversations, and I remain his most constant fan in spite of his E-reversal. He also told me that PABA, or para-aminobenzoic acid, is equally aphrodisiacal. I might point out that PABA, in spite of its formidable name, is a part of the B complex of vitamins, and, if you read my first book, *The Natural Way to Super Beauty,* you will know that B complex is so complex it must *never* be separated into its parts. This means that, no matter how you long for that turn-on vitamin, *do not* turn PABA out of its complex B-vitamin whole. It will do you no good—or at least nowhere near as much—and could do you a lot of harm if you take one part without the other, since too much of one part of the B-complex causes a depletion of the other parts. It's a tricky and complex B vitamin, to be handled with care. For the benefit of those who did not read *Super Beauty,* I will give the B-complex formula once more . . . this time I hope you will all study it carefully. If your B-complex does not contain the B's in this ratio, then simply buy the components separately, do a bit of mathematical calculation, and come up with the missing parts you need to complete the perfect B-complex whole.

If your B-complex contains 2 milligrams of B-1 it should contain *equal* amounts of B-2 and folic acid, meaning 2 milligrams of those. It should contain ten times as much pantothenic acid, or 20 milligrams. It should contain twenty times more PABA, or 40 milligrams. It should contain *500* times as much inositol and choline, or 1,000 milligrams. And, surprise, the B-12 you really need only amounts to 1 to 3 *micrograms.* Then I add 50 milligrams of B-6 for "slim."

Now, I've had so many questions on the business of B, that one would think you guys out there just didn't bother to read. It's easier to telephone the author. Well, it isn't that I don't love talking to you, but you may as well face the fact that, after a book on *this* subject, I'm going to be a lot harder to find. And, with the plethora of calculator toys about, you should have no trouble with your multiplication tables. I *can* tell you that your health food stores have vitamins already put together for you containing this B formula. The Plus Formula line has two. On the other hand, before you ask me, I'll tell you what *I* take. I take my all-time Allbee with C, prescribed twenty years ago by my physician, only now I supplement it with all the extra B's I need according to this formula. I intend to abide by it for as long as it works for me.

That should tell you everything you could dream up to ask. OK?

And that's enough about me and B. The point is that B is basic to anyone's good health, and good health is basic to Super Sex. Have you ever seen a sickly sexy body? No? I thought not. To be Super Sexual you must be in super shape—not just shapely-shape but healthy, strong and energetic shape as well. Which is exactly where we intend to put you. With the proper diet and the proper (note that word "proper") exercises, you'll be in shape for whatever situation arises—in bed or out.

Back to vitamin E. Yes, I'd like to get back to that, but I must have been blessed with an overabundance at birth. Because *I* find that if I take much vitamin E as a supplement, well, I end up crawling the walls unless I have my superman by my side day and night. And, as I've said, I have to work *sometime* and so does he, so it's E that goes out for me when it's in a capsule. (I've got lots of other uses for it.) More on that later. This does not mean it must go out for you. On the contrary. If you say you're "too tired for sex" (which I cannot conceive of anyone's being), then try taking dosages of 1,200 units per day and then come back a month later and tell me that. I'll never believe it. You'll doubtless have your partner begging for mercy unless you feed him/her the same amount, and don't say you weren't forewarned.

I think vitamin E is the miracle vitamin of the decade. I also think you must watch it, since they (meaning the researchers who work on such things) are now delving into the possibility of E build-up, meaning it could build up in the body just the way vitamins A and D can do. Those two are dangerous indeed if you get self-smart and dose yourself beyond the point considered safe by the experts. With vitamin A, that's 50,000 units per day (that's what *I've* taken for twenty years now, with no visible ill effects) and for vitamin D, make it 20,000 units (that's I.U.s, or international units) *weekly*, which should be more than enough, even when there's no sunshine in sight.

If, indeed, vitamin E has a build-up factor, they haven't found it yet, but to play it safe, don't go beyond the now-believed-safe dosage of 1,200 units per day. I always advise starting with 400 and, if that doesn't do the trick, progressing to 800 and finally 1,200—if, and only if, E, the famous sex vitamin, hasn't already done its sexual work. My bet is that, around 800, *anybody* will be satisfied. If not, carry on to 1,200 and stop.

One of the best possible foods anyone can eat—and I say this unequivocally (wouldn't skip a day without it)—is raw wheat germ. The "raw" part throws a lot of people, but I'll swear you'll soon get used to the nutty flavor. And when you see the results turning up in your sex life (and in your skin, in your hair—which it just plain *grows*) you'll soon forgo the more crunchy taste of toasted wheat germ for the raw. You see, any sort of heating process kills much of the vitamin content of any food—which is why I always opt for raw vegetables whenever possible. By the same token, crunchy, toasty wheat germ isn't going to have nearly as much of the same vitamin-punch as the raw. Put your taste buds behind you and think about your sex life. Wheat germ contains vitamin E. Get on with the wheat germ.

My information, which comes from all the food experts in the business of telling it like it is—Adelle Davis, Linda Clark, and others—says that wheat germ contains vitamin E. In spite of the lack of research done to prove it doesn't, I'd like to keep on believing it does. What-ever it contains, it works wonders.

In case anyone has any doubts as to the value of wheat germ for *every-one's* sex-benefit, here is a letter to Abigail van Buren, much better known as "Dear Abby," reprinted in its entirety:

Dear Abby:

This is for D., who was concerned about her male friend because he carried his own salad dressing in a little jar and sprinkled wheat germ in his food.

D's main concern should be keeping up with him in the bedroom. I don't know about the salad dressing, but I know a man who uses wheat germ regularly on his cereal and he's dynamite in that depart-ment. [Signed]—B.

I have to confess to probably shying a bit myself from a man who goes about with a bottle of salad dressing . . . but "B" certainly can (obviously) back me up on the sexy-making benefits of eating the germ of the wheat. So what are you waiting for?

There are other foods that are E-ful as well—sunflower seeds, nuts and the like. They make wonderful nibbling foods if nibble you must (I disapprove). At least you'll be gaining something besides pounds.

Then there's lecithin—that lovely stuff that helps make you thin, thin—which also just happens to be one of the primary food sources of vitamin E as well as the best possible source of the B vitamins choline and inositol. Those B vitamins are the best possible ones for your hair. And, be you male or female, to be Super-Sexy it helps to have sexy hair. Ask any man or woman. There's one little point I would like to add. Ninety percent of male semen is lecithin. Does that tell you anything? I didn't even suggest how you get it, but am simply pointing out a fact. You take it from there.

As you can see, this has turned into a health lecture, which it wasn't meant to be except, as I keep saying, I can't seem to separate health and sex, just as I can't separate sex from beauty (a point over which editors and I have argued, and which no editor has ever won). There simply is no way to separate these all-important factors that go into making the Super-Sexual creature that is *you.*

Therefore, look to your health, take care with what and how you eat, pop vitamins instead of any other kind of pill, and then stand back and watch the change in the vigorous, vital, virile and sexy creature you become.

THE BEAUTY OF SUPER SEX

It Shows
in Every Pore

I asked a famous New York dermatologist why it was that good sex made good skin. He swore he didn't know. He *did* say that the sexual flush is a real thing, meaning that the blood vessels dilate, allowing the skin to be flooded with blood carrying all sorts of good things to feed your skin. Then the doctor went on to say that constant flushing wouldn't be good. I had to smother a giggle, since even the Super-Sexiest people I know can't keep it coming *constantly*. Besides, this particular doctor has magnificent skin, and I've seen him with some pretty dishy chicks. I'm drawing my own conclusions, but I'd be willing to bet his sex life is pretty OK. (Doctors will never tell.)

Then I asked one of the most renowned of all make-up men—one with a name known round the world of beautiful women. He said, "I don't know, but it does." He let me down too. Perhaps there is no explanation. In other words, just do, and don't ask why. At that moment, this man's assistant appeared to see what we were discussing. I told her I wanted to know why good sex made good skin. Her reply? Good skin makes good sex *easier to get*! And she's right. Again, there's no way out of the circular bit when it comes to sex and beauty. Sex is good, skin is good. Skin is good—sex may not be yet, but, as this young lady put it, with pimples it takes longer to find.

Therefore, I'll give you the rudiments of healthy skin care, so that you need never let a pimple keep you out of bed and so that your sex life will show in every pore of your smooth, calm, relaxed, tranquil, unlined, happy face.

Don't think I'm talking cosmetics, now. I'm not. I'm talking basically beautiful skin, and that goes for you, Mr. America, as well as any woman. Pimply men are no more sexy than pimply women, and since teen-age pimples are simply not necessary on adults, let's take care of them.

Good skin means, first of all, clean skin. I'll grant you that women have to wear make-up and therefore have to take it off, but you men needn't think you'll ever get away with *no* care for your face. I have seen men in their fifties who don't do any of the right things and therefore end up with unsexy pimples. At fifty? Some turn-off. And no way to get into a Super-Sexual situation.

Men have one advantage women don't have, although they may not see it as such, and that is whiskers. I've been told by the experts that one reason men often look far younger than their years is because of the shaving they do each day. The weird facial exercises necessary for reaching inaccessible parts of the beard gives them built-in facial hold-ups. Not only that, some people have even suggested it's the whiskers themselves that make men less quick to go for the surgical face-lift. Whatever is true, it seems to be factual that manly faces appear less prone to wrinkles and lines. Maybe because, until the sexual revolution, men had everything going for them and women didn't. Just a guess. Perhaps now that women are Super Sexual too, the plastic surgery guys will have no business. Fine, since I prefer a naturally firm skin to any cut-and-sewn face.

When it comes to getting perfect skin and keeping it, the first step is to keep it clean. That means soap and water. Men use it usually because it comes naturally with shaving. Unfortunately, too many women go the "I have dry skin" route and refuse to cleanse with the only thing that really cleans, and that is water. Water, let's face it, is the only possible moisturizer. Commercial moisturizers are products designed to hold the water inside the skin. Unfortunately, too many commercial moisturizers tend to be offhand about the matter, occasionally coming up with a formula that dries rather than moisturizes. One of the most common ingredients in moisturizers is glycerine, but one iota too much glycerine takes away moisture rather than keeping it where it belongs—inside of your skin.

My skin-mentor, Dr. Erno Laszlo, who was, before his death a few years ago, the beauty-maker to all the Beautiful People, once said, "If God had not made water, I would have had to invent it." He was criticized a lot for that remark, but, by God, he was right. Water, and the holding of it within the skin, is the only answer to that traditional cop-out to creams, "I've got dry skin." According to Dr. Albert Kligman, Professor of Dermatology at the University of Pennsylvania, some women have less moisture than others, it seems, although no one has ever been able to do a measurement to prove it. If, however, tightness is what women are describing as a synonym for "dry," then they're the lucky ones, for tight skin means never having to say "I need a face-lift." It's just like a firm body—desirable, necessary and beautiful.

Here I have to go into a little rap on exactly what makes skin and what makes skin beautiful. Skin is pure protein—or at least 97 percent protein. Need I say that skin feeds on protein? Skin also is acid. You are as acid outside as inside (yes, you're acid inside) and never ever forget that, for the sake of your health as well as your beauty. Skin wears its acid mantle exactly that way—as a mantle for the protection of the skin from the bacteria that can get under it and cause unsightly blemishes (those pimples that, as my friend said, make it take longer to find Super Sex).

Therefore, *anything* that goes onto the skin *must be acid balanced*. In my opinion, the pH (acid) balance of any skin product is the most valuable and important thing to know. The heck with what the ads tell you about velvety complexions if you just slather such and such a hormone cream on nightly. The truth is that anything that is alkaline stands a good chance of doing a great deal of harm to your complexion by destroying the acid balance nature put there on purpose. And, as usual, nature has it all over man when it comes to knowing what's best for us and our looks. If we didn't go about mucking things up with our own man-made inventions, we'd all be better off. And better looking.

So we'll start with cleaning skin the acid-balanced way. There are, now, many acid-balanced soaps on the market. RedKen's strawberry-scented pink Beauty Bar is possibly the most famous. Jheri Rhedding has his Milk 'n Honee Bar, and others are appearing almost daily in drugstores and health food shops. There is one infallible way to test for the acidity of your soap. There are little papers called Nitrazine that can be purchased from any pharmacy. They are the acid test. *Never let your household be without them.* For they work like litmus paper in a chemistry classroom . . . if a substance is alkaline, i.e., death to your skin-beauty, the paper, dipped in that substance, turns bright blue. Throw the substance away as fast as blue appears. If the substance— soap, make-up, so-called moisturizers—is properly acid balanced, the Nitrazine paper won't change color at all, remaining its natural wheat color. That is the color for you. Natural. That is the color that will keep watch over your naturally beautiful skin (hair too, as we'll see later).

Therefore, whether salespeople think you a "kook" or not, what do you care? It isn't their sex lives you're thinking of, it's yours. Dip your Nitrazine into anything you're dreaming of putting onto your skin, and blue must be refused.

After the publication of *The Natural Way to Super Beauty*, I kept getting letters and calls asking me, "How do I wash my face?" I thought I had spelled it out perfectly, but I am going to do so again. As I told you, I won't be easy to find after this book—no listed phone, you can imagine. So here goes:

For washing your face—and wash you must, at least twice a day . . . once in the morning, once before retiring (a third time, before dressing for an evening out, is optional, but I can't imagine you'd want to take off for an evening with any would-be sexual partner without clean skin):

Fill your basin (clean that basin first!) with hot water—as hot as your hands can stand. Wet your face and neck. Then wet your acid-balanced soap and work it all over your face and neck, making a lather and rubbing that in also. Now rinse by splashing the *soapy* (that's what I said) water from the basin a *minimum* of thirty times all over your face and neck. If you still feel slithery, keep splashing until you're sure you're all rinsed. Dry with a *soft* towel by patting, not rubbing. In fact, no rubbing should ever be done to any facial skin . . . it's simply too delicate for such rough treatment, especially the skin around the eyes. Keep a light touch.

There. You have clean, acid-balanced skin.

There is one other option, one which I have used because—would you believe?—Dr. Laszlo, the one who came up with the acid-balanced theory forty years ago, had a soap that was alkaline! He wasn't around for me to ask why, but the answer I got from his chemists was that alkaline soap cleans better. I never questioned it too much, since my own skin was thriving on the Laszlo treatment. The thing was that Dr. Laszlo immediately put the acid back onto the skin with his after-wash treatment, and that treatment varied from individual to individual, so don't ask me what my own treatment was, since it might be all wrong for you. My answer to anyone's needs, if they choose to use alkaline soap, is the simple acid after-rinse. This can be simply accomplished by refilling *the cleaned-once-more* basin with more hot water and dropping into it either a few drops (please note I said *"few drops,"* and that is precisely what I mean) of your omnipresent cider vinegar, or lemon juice. I promise you, you won't go away smelling vinegary or like a lemon—not when it's a few drops in an entire basin of water, and that is exactly how diluted it ought to be unless you want to burn up your face with acid. That, we do not want. Then rinse as thoroughly as before—thirty times, no less—to put the acid back on as quickly as possible. Just make sure you never go out without your acid mantle on your skin.

Now. The washing routine I have just given you is basic cleansing. Someone is going to say it dries out his/her skin. And it might. For some people have skin that is over-oily—meaning they have overly active sebaceous glands secreting far too much of the skin's natural oils —while some have underactive ones. For those with underactive glands, the washing should go as follows:

Before washing, soak a cotton pad about the size of a quarter in wheat germ oil. You'll be putting on vitamin E and cutting down on the too-tightening effects (for you underactive-sebaceous types) of soap-*sans*-oil. Oil your face and neck thoroughly with the wheat germ oil. (Some prefer other nonsaturated oils such as grape seed, cotton seed and saf-flower. I still opt for wheat germ.) Once you are well oiled, begin the wash routine as described, rinsing and all.

If—after oiling and washing, your skin should ever become really rough, red and truly uncomfortable, then you may need to add a bit of cream. This is permitted for some, *but only after you've looked at your skin with a newly trained eye.*

As I've said, you have to get used to that tightened-up feeling. It took me six months to catch on to the fact that my skin was responding to its new right-kind-of (for once) treatment, and although it was six months before I could open my mouth without that stretched feeling, miraculously my skin took care of itself by balancing back into a normal skin, clear and blemish-free and no longer too tight. If it didn't feel somewhat tight, I'd begin to worry and get back to a more stringent tighten-up regimen, possibly leaving off any creams or oils. For the moment, it seems normal.

Therefore, you must learn to check your skin objectively, remembering that *tightness is much to be desired* and youthful beauty will be the long-term result. If you still feel you need cream, do the following: Check out some of the companies with advertised acid-balanced products (double-checking with your own Nitrazine paper to be sure. I never trust advertisements to tell the truth), and find a cream that you are sure is acid. Once you've found that you may really need it, after washing, *pat* some of the cream around your eyes and on your throat. Blot under eyes and neck ever so gently. If you still have red, rough, or peeling skin, use the cream over the entire face and neck, *always* rinsing it off with your vinegar or lemon after-rinse, *except* under your eyes and throat, where you must blot gently and carefully with a tissue. This puts your skin right where you want it . . . ever so slightly creamed, acid rinsed and tightened up. This entire treatment, I hasten to add, applies to men, women, and children. If more children (they shouldn't be reading this book—you tell them!) were started on the right road to beautiful skin when they were still babes, we'd have a lot less teen-age skin trouble and a lot happier teen-agers. But, as I said, teen-agers should keep out of this book for a few more years. I'll leave it to any readers who are parents to pass along the treatment. Save on the dermatologist bills, remember?

I hope that this time I have gotten the clean-routine to you in the clearest possible manner. Soap and water, basic. Especially for oily skin. Oil, soap and water—basic for underactive, or less oily skin. Oil, soap, and water and acid-balanced cream—*basic for extreme cases only*, but: *everything followed by your acid after-rinse.* Is that clear? I hope so. If beautiful skin helps you find Super Sex faster, I'd suggest you get on with it. And, I must confess my super men have super skin.

Now that we're over the basic beauty hump, we're on to the sexy skin question. Why is it that Super Sexy lives make for super skin? Man, have I had trouble with the skin folk on that one. The answers are still at large, although virtually every dermatologist, make-up person, or skin specialist questioned agreed with the fact that a Super Sex life makes super skin. The consensus seems to be that Super Sex makes for a super life, meaning super relaxation and non-tension (thus no tension lines), and that all of these factors are what make the skin beautiful. The simple answer in my own mind is that beauty is as beauty feels, and a Super Sex life is the only Dr. Feelgood to fool around with. It seems to be the key to all beauty—body-beauty, skin-beauty, hair-beauty, and beauty that radiates from within, attracting more Super Sex to the already Super-Sexual being that you should be by now. And so around and around we go. If you keep on with Super Sex, you'll keep getting it more and more and looking all the better for it, and I, for one, can't think of a more delightful way to work on one's looks. I intend to get in all the practice possible for as long as I live. And, if what the doctors say is true, that will be a long time, if my Super Sex life continues. Here's hoping.

A SEXY-SKIN POSTSCRIPT

A "lady of the night" of my acquaintance (except that most of her work is done by day) tells me that she actually uses male semen on her skin for a tighten-upper. Wow! As far as I am concerned that is a pretty far-out use for what I would much prefer to have where it belongs, namely, in my vagina, which is the point from which the beauty of sexual skin begins. I'm giving you her idea, however, to use if and when you see fit.

WHAT DOES YOUR SKIN WEAR TO BED?

Its acid mantle. Period. I cannot believe the numbers of people who ask me whether they should put on make-up for bed. First of all, your skin will be radiant enough so that you don't need make-up to hide *anything*. The best compliment my man ever paid me was one (day) in bed when he patted my face and said, "You're not wearing any make-up." Startled, I said, "I have on everything." And he said, "It doesn't feel like it." Terrific, because that's the clue to natural skin beauty. Naturally beautiful skin. Once you've balanced it into perfect shape, you won't be able to see the difference between night and day.

Of course I don't want you putting on make-up for bed. But I *do* insist that you do your cleansing routine exactly as laid out for you, ending with the gently blotted acid rinse. Then you are off to bed wearing your acid mantle and little else. He'll only know you look gorgeous. You take it from there.

Hair, Hair!—
Plus a Great Exercise
for Circulation

When it comes to healthy hair, you must never forget that your circulation is the thing that gets healthy blood to a healthy scalp and therefore makes healthy hair. The exercises shown in this chapter will improve your circulation. All of those wherein the head hangs down will go to your head, and so to your hair. You must remember as well that scalp is skin, so what is good for the scalp is also good for the skin. Getting the blood running at the top is the answer to making skin and hair lovelier. (Super Sex is a super circulator.)

Hair has been a classic sex symbol since Godiva used her long locks for a little bit of modesty. These days, hair is as much of a sex symbol for males as for females, in fact, I'm not sure there aren't more locker-room television commercials for baby shampoo than there are babies in those things.

Point is, you've gotta treat your hair well to keep it looking "come-on." The very first thing you must learn is that hair, like you, is pure (97 percent pure) protein, and that ought to tell you how much protein means to the health, and looks, of your locks.

The next thing that may surprise you, but *will* save your hair, is that hair, like you, is acid. This means that anything that goes onto your hair must be acid, just like what goes on your skin.

You test out your shampoo exactly the same way you test out your skin-care products—with that handy little Nitrazine paper. If it's blue, it's through for you—and your hair. Alkaline products—soap and other lousy shampoos that turn blue—will destroy the natural acidity of the hair and void its naturally protective acid mantle. Acid-balanced products, on the other hand, will manage to give you swinging, thicker, healthier and shinier hair. Don't ask me how they do it. They do. My own hair is living (and never forget that hair is a living, sexy part of you) proof of how proper hair care with a knowledgeable trichologist's (hair expert) help can turn straggly locks into a shining halo. It helps, even if it's bed-mussed. There's simply something about lots of it that turns people on. Check that one out yourselves.

Therefore, I'm going to see that you have a lot of it to throw about.

First start with clean. That's what hair must be, since it's part of your scalp, which is part of your skin and part of your face. Any dirt on your hair is going to do no good at all for your face. Therefore, whistle clean and a daily shampoo *will not hurt a bit*! I do mine every two days because I'm lazy, but two's the limit. There are more and more acid-balanced shampoos on the market, with RedKen and Jheri Redding still leading the pack (those Californians are always into healthy, sunny beauty). The big cosmetics moguls, however, have rapidly jumped onto the acidity bandwagon, recognizing a salable thing when they see it, even if they didn't dream up the idea. I don't care whose you use as long as it keeps your Nitrazine a neutral beige—pH-balanced. I happen to use acid-balanced soap at the moment, for I travel a lot and it's handier. It's nothing more than solidified shampoo and easy to pack. If you use the shampoo, however, there's a trick that does wonders for your hair and gives it a remarkable extra thickness to boot. Slice open a perle of 400 units of vitamin E and squeeze the liquid into your shampoo bottle. Shake thoroughly. You'll find the E not only seems to get under your skin but does a remarkable job of thickening your hair. One of those miracles of vitamin-nature.

Then we go on to protein, which usually goes hand in hand with the acid-balanced shampoos. In other words, the *good* protein shampoos are generally properly acid-balanced. Good, after all, is good. The thing about protein shampoo is that it must be *hydrolized* protein to work—meaning the molecules have been broken up into sizes that can actually be absorbed by the hair itself—otherwise it could be protein shampoo on your head, and egg on your face.

Don't be afraid to inquire about the protein in any brand of protein shampoo. Make them 'fess up as to whether it's hydrolized or not, and if the salesperson can't say, forget it. Protein that gets into your hair is the only kind that can work from the outside. Protein taken inside in the form of food is the other side of the hair-coin. It's got to be a do-gooder, and is the very thing that will give you more hair than ever.

I'll never forget when, in a moment of college-student stupidity, I gave up eating eggs. My hair became so thin it was see-through—and embarrassing. I had a knowledgeable hair-man who asked what it was I *wasn't* eating. When I replied "eggs" he was furious and commanded me back to them. The hair came back with the eggs. That's the power of protein for the health of your hair.

All protein (eggs at the top of the list) can go straight to your head, giving you the lovely, healthy head of hair you yearn for. It not only can, it will.

Fish, meat (I still disapprove of beef—fattening, and not the best protein), cheese, beans (especially soybeans), and wheat germ are all full of protein power, all are great hair-raisers.

Wheat germ is the most miraculous of the hair foods, as far as I'm concerned. (And it does just as much for your sex life, so how can you lose?) Hair-guru Vidal Sassoon vows he started the wheat-germ routine some twenty years ago for vitality (his hair is—naturally—beautiful), and when asked what it did for his sexuality, replied, "Ask Beverly" (his beautiful young wife). No complaints. There you are. I take three tablespoons of wheat germ each and every day—wouldn't go without it. My hair grows like that proverbial weed, and don't let anyone try to tell me hair only grows a quarter inch a year. My hairdresser can discount that.

Lecithin, that wonder of wonder-workers, which can be found in any health food store, is made from soybeans—so there's your protein right there while you're getting all the other benefits (litheness, for one) of lecithin. Lecithin simply does almost everything, from keeping you lithe to making sure you never hold in unnecessary water (it comes out naturally, like it should). Lecithin goes on top of my wheat germ each morning, in the measure of one tablespoonful—two if I'm feeling needy. Lecithin has calories, however, so if you're counting those, be sure to count in lecithin. For the low-carbohydrate diet, there's no worry, since lecithin is pure fat.

There's one final thing I have to say about hair. Get yours cut, regularly and by someone good. Whether you wear your hair short or long, keeping it unkempt means split ends, which will eventually travel right up to the roots, leaving no hair at all. Not very sexy. A regular trim by the hands of an expert will keep hair at its lovely healthiest—and do the same for you.

Enough said about hair-care except *do it*, and then use that hair to make yourself into the sexpot (or sex-jock) you want to be. We know from history that it works.

There's a lot to be said for knowing yourself upside down. One never knows the positions one can end up in. (Up-end in?) It is surprising how many people don't know their left hands from their right, once their heads are down and their legs up. To many it's a complete confusion and disorientation. Get over it. It can lead to some things that are plenty of fun. And getting over it means practice, naturally, so that the whole idea seems natural.

While you're turned upside down, you're improving your circulation, working on plenty of necessary-to-Super-Sex muscles, and reversing the pull of gravity—the better to make you look "up."

There is a simple and safe (and, boy, do I believe in "safe") way to do any upside-down exercise, and that is by using a wall as a support. This way *you* are supported but you have complete freedom of legs and hips and pelvic region (which we never want to forget), as well as virtually everything all the way up your back. While all of this is going on, you're relaxing—hard though that may be to believe. For anything that manipulates the spine is—afterward—going to make you as relaxed as a rag doll until you're ready to spring into action. Muscle-toned action, that is.

Lying on your back, with your fingers clasped behind your head, your elbows flat on the floor, begin—slowly—walking up the wall by raising your hips.

Press more with your left foot, slowly straightening your right leg and bringing it as close as possible to the floor behind your head. Careful! If it hurts, just go as far as you can, and then return it to the wall.

If it hasn't hurt yet, continue by placing your foot on the other knee and pressing *gently*. Return to the first position.

Now do the same thing with the other leg.

Still against the wall, legs up and apart, place your hands on your hips. Slowly, pressing with your feet against that omnipresent (it had better be) wall, contract the backs of your legs and buttocks until you

feel the muscles working, simultaneously tightening up your hips and lifting them. Hold this position for a few seconds while it works and works and works. Then, moving one foot after the other, bring your

feet together. Slowly, lower your hips. Inhale going up, exhale coming down. In all holding patterns, just breathe normally, but *breathe*!

Afterthoughts
(Home, Lovely Home)

All of my adult, on-my-own life has been spent in exactly four apartments. Two were big, beautiful and barren. Two were close, cluttered and cozy. I'll give you one guess as to which ones had the most sexual activity taking place.

Since you ladies do the decorating, don't do as I did and let decoration get in the way of your love life. For one thing, you can get so hung up on making things look lovely that you do as I did, and forget about love. My man almost got away. My decision was to move again.

There's something about a room that makes one feel exposed that can effectively kill anything resembling the closeness required for a great sexual relationship.

I'm a pretty good test case, since I've been with the same man through at least two of the four apartments. But now that I look back on my life—and it goes way back—I can trace the amount of good loving directly to the place in which it took place.

All those open spaces may seem seductive to you if you've been locked into tiny-apartment living. But they apparently don't seem so seductive to a man who's out to seduce you.

You might as well benefit from my bad experiences in this area rather than live through them yourselves.

A friend of mine, when he heard I was doing this book, said, "Be sure to tell those women to think of their men when they're decorating their bedrooms. It's disconcerting as hell to have a lot of ditsy little furniture that I'm afraid I might break."

Seems unimportant but it could be one of the most important moves in your sex life, that home of yours.

One of my own small, and therefore cozy, apartments was the source of a lot of self-doubts at one point in my life. Men kept attacking me. I began to question whether or not I might give off harlot-vibes and wept out my fears to a shrink-friend who had a wonderful solution for the problem: always greet guests wearing my coat and hat—ready to go. You see this was my very first apartment in a Manhattan brownstone— tiny, lantern-lit, palm tree-filled. That's all the furniture I could afford. In short, it was the picture of almost every first-apartment in Manhattan. Except for its peculiar seduction problems.

When I moved into my next large, beautiful, barren number, I longed for some of those attacks. The phone remained silent, men stayed away in droves, and I was yearning for "cozy."

The point is, there is a lot to be said for decor—but beware of being decorated. For one thing, decorators are generally more concerned with the outcome of the work than they are with the outcome of *your* work—which should be seduction, be you male or female.

Just don't let them overdo, especially if you're female, with that ditsy little furniture my friend so feared.

If you're a man, don't *you* overdo it either with the fur rugs and round beds, etc., unless you want to scare the devil out of any woman. Mirrored ceilings are a definite no, and are a pretty good giveaway to the fact that you know precious little about Super Sex—as yet. For when you're really involved, there's little time for staring into mirrors. I'm no ingenue. I know it's done, and there are those who say it's fun. I don't believe a word. If you're paying attention to the sex at hand— *really* paying attention—then you can't possibly be watching too.

One of the funniest stories I know concerning overdecoration hap- pened to a friend of mine who had set her cap for an eligible bachelor and arranged a dinner *à deux*, candles and all. She had carefully turned back the bed and decorated her apartment with, of all things, *black* candles.

When the gentleman arrived, he looked around and coolly said, "What is this, High Mass?" No seduction that night. Dinner was served.

Big, barren apartments bring in *no* men, as opposed to the tiny, two-by-fours that bring out the animal in all of them.

There must be something in between rape and celibacy. However, I've learned a lot through my redecoration traumas.

There are plenty of no-nos that you simply don't let any well-meaning decorator (or friend, family, whatever) get by with.

Such as:

Never have a sofa that is too delicate—either in reality or in looks or in fabric—to fall down on and make love on if the mood is on! For years I lived in a one-room apartment, laughingly called, by New York real-estate standards, a two-and-a-half-room apartment. And so, for years, my bed made do as a sofa, meaning there were thousands of cushions to make it halfway sittable. Also, thousands of cushions to be removed when one wished to retire. No matter. This poor bed of mine went through many transitional covers. The last was the most successful—a color that showed *nothing*, dark brown velvet that felt good even if you didn't pull it back. Sometimes I don't get the point in feeling you have to get between the sheets in order to work your way out of them again.

Finally my poor bed cover went to tatters. A friend said, "Why don't you just put it in the typewriter and let it do the book?" Believe me it could. But I'll swear to you, it went the way of that dilapidated diaphragm. That well-worn bed cover is preserved for posterity in my store room. Some things, I believe, should be kept just for luck.

Meanwhile, I have found, at last, a more-than-one-room apartment. I have a real-live sofa and it's covered in a light color and I'm just waiting to see how long it will last. But I'll swear I'll never give up love for a sofa.

For God's sake don't have something a man can't put his feet on if he wishes (I am questionably blessed with a lover who can't keep his feet on the ground)—not with his shoes on, one hopes, but if he does, don't find yourself thinking furniture before man.

I am watching my new home carefully. I am finding that parts of it are a bit awesome to some people. It is large—my breakout from all those years of shoe-boxing it—and roomy and high-ceilinged. I see some folks looking a bit fearful. If that keeps up, we'll lower the ceilings, or bring in some tall trees or something to close it up. People should feel cuddled in houses. People should be cuddled in houses. Remember the three F's. All should be possible in the home.

SEXTIME STORY

I hope, pray, fervently that each and every one of you by-now happy people have gotten the true picture of how important I feel Super Sex (not just any old sex) is to the state of your entire being.

Don't think there haven't been those who've made fun of my theory over the years. But guess who had the better life? Well, I think I did.

I can only hope that by now there isn't a soul with a hangup about anything sexual on this earth. Well, yes, I confess to a few hangups about things I personally consider aberrations. Talk those over with your own psychiatrist. One of those, I'm not.

But sex between two people (note the number) should be the supreme joy of life, with no guilt-strings attached. Took me years to cast off the "nice girls don't do that" sort of upbringing and start realizing that sex *is* life itself. What I hope you will do for yourselves is to focus on making your own sex lives *the most important part of your lives*. After that, any problems that arise practically solve themselves. You'll soon see. I happen to feel that Super Sex makes for a super life, and that's what I want us all to have. Then the Super-Sexual revolution will have taken over and life will be as it should be—super-beautiful. Enjoy. *And keep practicing*!

Index